GEM TRAILS OF UTAH

by
James R. Mitchell

Gem Guides Book Co.
315 Cloverleaf Drive, Suite F
Baldwin Park, CA 91706

Library of Congress Catalog Card Number: 96-75814
ISBN 0-935182-87-X

Cover Photo: Region just west of the Fremont River collecting area

Introduction: James R. Mitchell and the
   Staff of the Lewis Rock Shop, Salt Lake City, Utah
Maps: Jean Hammond and John Mayerski
Cover: Mark Webber

NOTE:
   Due to the possibility of personal error, typographical error, misinterpre-
tation of information, and the many changes due to man or nature, *Gem
Trails of Utah*, its publisher and all other persons directly or indirectly associated with this publication assume no responsibility for accidents, injury or
any losses by individuals or groups using this publication.
   In rough terrain and hazardous areas all persons are advised to be aware
of possible changes due to man or nature that occur along the gem trails.

TABLE OF CONTENTS

4

MAP LEGEND

▬▬▬▬▬	Interstate Highway
▬▬▬▬▬	U.S. Highway
▬▬▬▬	State Highway
▬▬▬▬	Divided Highway
────────	Local Road
▬▬▭▬▭▬▬	Gravel Graded Road
═══════	Graded Dirt Road
= = = = = = =	Unimproved Dirt Road
— — — — — —	Trail
(15)	Interstate Highway
(50)	U.S. Highway
(12)	State Highway
[87]	Forest or County Road
⚒	Mine
≡	Cattle Guard
⊠	Gate
▲	Campground

KEY TO SITES ON MAP

PART I

REGION I:
(1)   Great Salt Lake
(2)   Delta
(3)   Silver Island Mountains
(4)   Painter Spring
(5)   Eureka
(6)   Silver City
(7)   Yuba Lake
(8)   Ophir and Mercur
(9)   Nephi
(10) Topaz Mountain
(11) Ponderosa Campground
(12) Dugway
(13) Vernon

REGION II:
(14) Woodland
(15) Birdseye
(16) Silver Creek Junction

REGION III:
(17) Long Valley Junction
(18) Kodachrome Basin
(19) Little Creek Mountain
(20) Summit
(21) Parowan
(22) Brian Head
(23) Agate Hill
(24) Panguitch
(25) Beaver
(26) Clear Lake
(27) Vermilion Cliffs
(28) Paria River
(29) Mt. Carmel
(30) Wah Wah Mountains
(31) Old Frisco
(32) West of Milford
(33) Black Rock
(34) Milford Area
(35) North of Milford
(36) Salina Canyon

REGION IV:
(37) Notom
(38) Caineville
(39) Factory Butte
(40) Fremont River
(41) West of Hanksville
(42) Hanksville
(43) Horse Canyon
(44) Spencer Flat
(45) Hell's Backbone
(46) Escalante
(47) Straight Cliffs
(48) Little Egypt
(49) Green River
(50) Crescent Junction
(51) Looking Glass Road
(52) La Sal Junction
(53) Moab
(54) Dubinky Well
(55) Cisco and Yellow Cat
(56) San Rafael
(57) Summerville Wash

PART II

REGION I:
(58) Tule Valley
(59) Levan
(60) Gold Hill

REGION III:
(61) Sawtooth Peak

REGION IV:
(62) Clay Hills
(63) Egg Canyon
(64) Harris Wash
(65) Lockhart Basin
(66) Potash Road
(67) Courthouse Pasture
(68) Willow Springs Wash

LOCATOR MAP

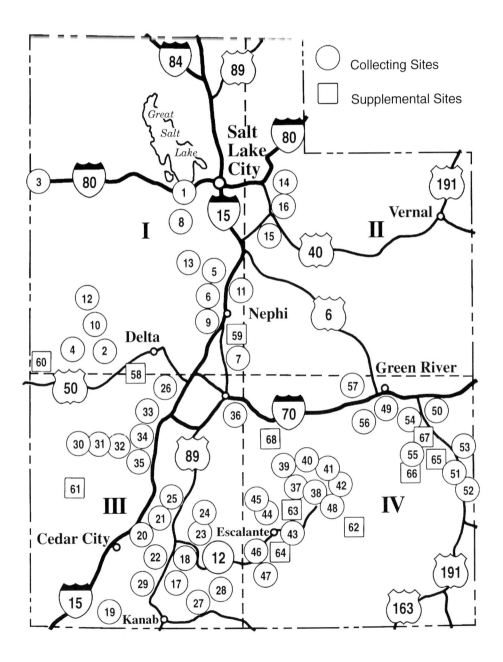

Collecting Sites

Supplemental Sites

Great Salt Lake

Salt Lake City

I

II

Vernal

Delta

Nephi

Green River

III

Cedar City

Escalante

IV

Kanab

INTRODUCTION

Welcome to rockhounding in Utah! You'll find many unique opportunities in Utah's 84,990 square miles. Utah mountains reach to a lofty 13,528 feet (King's Peak, Ashley National Forest). Basins sink to 2,200 feet (Beaver Dam Wash). The geographical variety provides for many types of rockhounding trips. Along with the latitude, geographical variety also explains the extreme temperatures. Winter mountains are frigid. Summer deserts parch. Knowing these extremes helps in planning trips.

This guidebook is intended to provide information related to mineral localities within the state of Utah which are available to amateur collectors and rockhounds. The sites are situated in areas as full of variety as the minerals themselves. The terrain includes pine-covered mountains, barren desert, and just about everything in between. In addition, your journeys will take you through spectacular scenery, historical sites and interesting cities and towns.

The sites listed in the revised *Gem Trails of Utah* were checked shortly before publication to verify mineral availability and to confirm that collecting was still allowed. In this edition, twenty-two new sites have been added, and many of the less productive ones from the past have been eliminated. It is also important to note that the maps are intentionally NOT DRAWN TO SCALE. The purpose is to have one illustration providing not only the general location setting, but also detailed travel instructions near the site itself.

Most of the areas discussed on the following pages are relatively easy to get to if you have appropriate transportation, but road conditions can change. Severe weather may make good roads very rough, and very rough roads impassable, even with four-wheel drive. Do not attempt traveling where your vehicle was not designed to go.

The book is divided into two parts. Part I gives detailed travel descrip-

Road to the Salina Canyon site

tions to fifty-seven specific collecting sites within the state of Utah. Each is accompanied by a detailed map and, in most cases, a photograph. Mileage is as accurate as possible, but odometers on all vehicles do vary and distances have been rounded to the nearest tenth of a mile.

Part II describes an additional eleven sites which the author has not yet personally visited or they were so vast that no exact spot could be pinpointed for good mineral concentration. Each site, however, has been verified by reliable sources. In Part II photographs and precise travel instructions may not be provided. These sites should still be productive, possibly even more than those listed in Part I, and will be of interest to those willing to spend some additional time and effort.

ROCK & MINERAL HIGHLIGHTS

Utah has a plethora of rocks and minerals to collect, but some stand out in the crowd. A few of the rocks and minerals described below are no longer available for collecting. They are included here because they are what help to make Utah unique geologically. All of the rocks and minerals described can be purchased at rock shops or viewed at natural history museums.

Topaz

Topaz, the state gem, is still found in quantity at Topaz Mountain in the Thomas Range. Crystals from this site range from one-quarter inch to several inches long. The most prized among facetors and mineral collectors alike are the uniquely colored sherry crystals. Much more common are clear and brown crystals. Finding nice specimens requires hard digging. This is one place a hammer, chisel, and safety goggles are a must. For enjoyment without the work, look in the gullies and fields. This will yield small quartz-like crystals. These crystals are topaz bleached by the sun.

Red Beryl

The beryl family includes emeralds and aquamarines. Red beryl, also known as red emerald, is a very rare form of beryl found exclusively in Utah. The first reported occurrence of red beryl was at Topaz Mountain. At Topaz Mountain cloudy quarter-inch specimens are found as single crystals or roses, sometimes perched on topaz crystals. The most distinguished red beryls, however, come from the Wah Wah Mountains south of Topaz Mountain. Here red beryls grow several inches in length, and are often gem quality. Their color is a deep red unmatched by any other gemstone. Red beryl sites are all privately claimed. No collecting is permitted. Specimens are displayed at local museums and rock shops.

Bixbyite

Bixbyite is an iron-manganese oxide. The crystals form as one-eighth to almost one inch shiny metallic cubes with all the corners trimmed. Named after Maynard Bixby, a famous Utah mineralogist, this mineral is sought by collectors from around the world. It is found all along the Thomas Range and is easily collected in Topaz Cove at Topaz Mountain. Bixbyite is found occasionally on or with topaz or red beryl.

Fluorite

Calcium fluoride forms in a multitude of colors including white, violet, blue, red, black, pink, and colorless. It was named for its fluorescent properties, usually blue-white, under a long-wave light. One of the most famous Utah occurrences is at the Deer Trail Mine, a private claim, in Piute County. At the mine fluorite is found as pale green (sometimes with a bluish tint) dodecahedral crystals.

Flourite forms around hot springs and in hydrothermal veins. It is associated with quartz, galena, barite and various other hydrothermal vein minerals. Collectors can locate flourite specimens at several locations including the Milford area, Sawtooth Peak and the area surrounding Ophir and Mercur.

Azurite

Azurite, a blue copper carbonate, is found in many locations in Utah. Azurite is found in the old mining region surrounding what used to be the town of Silver City along with numerous other secondary copper minerals. In the Milford area azurite occurs along with chrysocolla, malachite and bornite. The mine dumps near the once bustling town of Gold Hill also boast nice specimens of azurite.

Two of the most famous locations are both privately held claims. At the Dixie-Apex Mine, in the Beaver Dam area, stable azurite and malachite stalactites and stalagmites have been found along with other formation types. Azurite in the form of nodules or "blueberries" is found in the La Sal Mountains in southeast Utah.

Obsidian

Several locations throughout the state offer gem quality obsidian that is an excellent source of material for lapidary work. North of Milford the ground is covered with obsidian, most of which is black. Mahaghony and snowflake material can also be found in the area.

In the Black Rock region black, mahaghony and snowflake specimens can be found in sizes ranging from pebbles to boulders. Pieces of obsidian large enough to turn six-inch spheres are easily collected. South of Beaver it can be found in a variety of colors and patterns.

Variscite

Variscite is a rare, green, hydrated, phosphate of aluminum and iron. It is found only in a handful of locations worldwide. Utah boasts three variscite deposits, all of which are privately held, and not open for collecting. Clay Canyon, near Fairfield, holds the most sought after variscite in the world. At Clay Canyon it forms in nodules that are often a deep emerald green color with very interesting patterns within the nodules. Other variscite locations in Utah are Ametrice Hill, also near Fairfield, and Lucin, on the Utah-Nevada border west of the Great Salt Lake.

Dugway Geodes

The Dugway Geode Beds are a wonderful place to visit. The geodes range from one-half inch to several feet in diameter (extremely rare). The geode beds are unconsolidated sand and gravel. Be careful to avoid digging a steep incline or cave as a hazardous condition will result.

The most commonly found geodes are three to four inches in diameter. They have a sugary grain coating of quartz crystals inside, with an occasional quartz scepter. Geodes that are more rare include those filled with amethyst, fluorite, and barite.

The geode beds are along the Pony Express Trail southwest of Salt Lake City. There are lots of historic and natural sights to enjoy while in this area.

Septarium Nodules

Septarium nodules are an unusual type of concretion formed as a mud ball shrinks and cracks as it dries. Calcite then fills in the concretion resulting in beautiful patterns formed by the mud and calcite. Occasionally a complete calcite crystal is found in a hollow. Septarium nodules have also been known to form around pelecypods or gastropods.

Nice quality septarium nodules are found near Alton at the Long Valley Junction area. The hills west of Orderville (the Mt. Carmel site) are also a source of Utah's best known mineralogical export, the septarium nodule. The occasional nodule can also be found near Burro Seep, only a few miles south of Crescent Junction.

Halite

Halites are beautiful yellow and white salt formations found around the Great Salt Lake, especially along the northern and southern shores. The Great Salt Lake boasts an average salt content of twenty-five percent, compared to sea water's three percent. With that immense concentration, the situation is perfect for crystallization, especially in regions of evaporation, or around submerged twigs or rocks.

Stansbury Island, a peninsula situated about thirty-five miles west of Salt Lake City offers good access for collecting beautiful examples of halite crystals. On the Bonneville Salt Flats, west of the Great Salt Lake large, halite crystals, several inches in size, are found growing on rocks, bushes, twigs, train tracks and just about anything else that is stationary.

Ultraviolet Minerals

Ultraviolet minerals are abundant in Utah. Some of the most popular minerals include austinite and cuproadamite from Gold Hill, chalcedony with traces of beryllium from the Thomas Range, chalcedony within geodes from Dugway, and petrified wood and agates from throughout the state. Rockhounding with a UV light is a lot of fun. Many things besides minerals fluoresce, too, such as scorpions, snakes, and spiders.

UTAH GEOLOGY

The state of Utah can be sectioned into three geologic provinces: the Colorado Plateau, the Middle Rocky Mountains, and the Basin and Range Province.

The Colorado Plateau

The Colorado Plateau is a high altitude desert characterized by mesas, canyons, and sloping pediments. It is located is the southeast quadrant of the state. Presently, not much in the way of collectable minerals are found there. In the past uranium, azurite, coal, gypsum and celestite were mined commercially in this area.

Geologically this area has a lot to offer. The Colorado Plateau is home to over sixteen national monuments, state parks, and recreational areas, including Rainbow Bridge and Canyonlands National Park.

The Middle Rocky Mountains

The Middle Rocky Mountains in the northeast quadrant of the state contain the Uinta Mountains, a very rare east-west trending mountain range, and the Wasatch Range, a north-south trending range. These ranges are high mountains with evergreen vegetation. Utah's highest peak is in the Uinta Mountains at King's Peak.

The Uinta Mountains and Wasatch Mountains intersect near Park City. The geology of the area is highly complex and of interest to gem and mineral hunters. Park City has a rich mining history. The mining dumps still hold collectable specimens, although most are closed to collectors.

The Basin and Range Province

The Basin and Range Province covers the western half of the state. It is a north-south trending set of ranges and valleys caused by a stretching in the Earth's crust (plate tectonics). The area is characterized by desert vegetation such as sagebrush, cedar, and tumbleweed. Snakes and scorpions are a common problem for collectors in this area. The Basin and Range Province is home to Topaz Mountain and the Dugway Geode Beds, as well as many other excellent collecting locations.

MINING HISTORY

Descriptions of Utah are filled with the words "unique" and "varied" and they apply to Utah's mining history as well. Mormons, properly called Latter Day Saints, settled the Salt Lake Valley as an agricultural community. The mining industry wasn't long in following, however, and salt was collected from the Great Salt Lake almost from the time pioneers arrived in 1847.

In 1854 a reward was offered by the Territorial Legislature for the discovery of a commercial-size coal deposit. In 1865 coal was available commercially from Coalville.

An abandoned mine near the once booming town of Old Frisco

Ironically the pioneers that settled the Salt Lake Valley did not stake the first mining claims. United States soldiers stationed at Fort Douglas (Salt Lake City) found ore and established the West Mountain Mining District in the Oquirrh Mountains in September of 1863. The Oquirrh Mountains still host commercial mining over 100 years later. Coal, copper, gold, silver, lead, oil, uranium and zinc became Utah's prominent mineral yield.

MINING DISTRICTS

There are many locations to explore in Utah. Always ask permission before entering private property. Never enter an abandoned mine, there are always plenty of good specimens to be found on the dumps. Respect private claims and don't collect in unauthorized or posted areas.

Collecting areas can be described as mining districts and Utah has several districts of interest to collectors.

The Bingham District

The Bingham district is located in the Oquirrh Mountains, west of Salt Lake City. It houses the largest man-made excavation in the world. Bingham Canyon Mine is one-half mile deep and covers 1,900 acres. At the top it is nearly two and one-half miles across. Since 1906, five billion tons of material have been removed from the mine. According to the Kennecott Corporation, owner of Bingham Canyon Mine, approximately two-thirds of all Utah mineral production comes from the mine. Although the area is famous for copper, many other materials such as lead, zinc, silver, gold, molybdenum and almost one hundred other minerals are extracted here. Many rare and aesthetic minerals are found in this area. Collecting is prohibited, but a visitor's center is open to the public April through October.

The Tintic District

The Tintic District is located in Eureka and produces many spectacular specimens. In particular, the Hidden Treasure Mine is famous for its aurichalcites and related minerals. There are literally hundreds of abandoned mines. Do not enter abandoned mines, as they can be extremely dangerous. The dumps of these mines are littered with hidden treasures of their own and supply plenty of collecting .

The Tintic Mining District was discovered in the late 1860s and today over eighty minerals may be found by collectors. Most minerals in this district are sulfides, sulfosalts and a few of the more rare tellurides.

Gold Hill District

Gold Hill is southeast of Wendover. It is of interest to mineral collectors because of the variety of copper arsenate minerals found there. Adamite, austinite and conichalcite are some of the more common minerals found in this area. They are easy to collect in open pits at the top of the mountain. The South Pit produces the austinite and adamite, whereas the adjoining pit to the north, the Glory Hole, produces conichalcite on the walls of the pit. Be alert for rattlesnakes as you explore the area.

More rare and completely unique minerals also come from this mine, but are mostly found underground. Collecting these minerals should be left to professionals who have permission to collect them. A visit to a local natural history museum or rock shop will allow collectors to see and acquire the unique specimens from this area.

The Uinta (Park City) District

Mining in Park City began in the late 1800s. Over fifteen million dollars in gold, silver, copper, lead and zinc came from Park City. This area has also produced four-inch dodecahedron pyrite specimens, some of the largest in the world. Almost all mines and mine dumps, however, have been posted no collecting.

The Thomas Range

The Thomas Range in western central Utah is a world class producer of prized minerals such as red beryl, topaz, garnet, chalcedony, amethyst, ilmenite, fluorite, calcite, cassiterite and durangite.

These minerals occur throughout the entire Thomas Range, which is composed of a rhyolitic lava and ash. Multiple eruptions built up the thick layer rhyolite. Later, ground water and gases bubbling up through the rhyolite produced pockets that were eventually lined with crystals.

ROCKHOUNDING RULES

This book is intended as a guide for reference. IT DOES NOT GIVE PERMISSION TO COLLECT! Information was accurate at the time it was submitted to the publisher. If you have a suspicion that a particular site is no longer open, be sure to ascertain the situation before trespassing. If nothing can be determined locally, land ownership information is available at the County Recorder's office. Please use common sense at any collecting sight because conditions and rules change.

Almost 67% of Utah land is governed by the Bureau of Land Management. Casual collecting, that is small amounts of rocks, minerals and invertebrate fossils for personal use, is allowed on BLM land. Petrified wood collection is limited to 25 pounds per day per person plus one piece, with a maximum of 250 pounds per person per calendar year. The BLM does issue commercial permits for larger amounts. Keep in mind that no vertebrate fossils may be collected on BLM land.

State collection rules are more strict. A rockhounding permit similar to a fishing license is required for all collecting on state land. With a permit, collectors can take up to 25 pounds plus one piece per person per day with a maximum of 250 pounds per year of all types of rock material except fossils. Collecting is not allowed in state and local parks. Current permit information is available from the State School and Institutional Trust Lands Administration, 355 West North Temple, 3 Triad Center, Suite 400, Salt Lake City, UT 84116, (801) 538-5508.

For current fossil collecting information contact the State Paleontologist at 300 Rio Grande, Salt Lake City, Utah, 84104, (801) 533-3513.

Some safety guidelines apply to every rockhounding expedition.

1. Research the site before visiting. Use guides such as this one, talk to people who have been there, and make use of the expertise of museum and rock shop staffs in the area.
2. Always take and use equipment and clothing appropriate to the site.
3. Use the buddy system. Don't collect alone. Let someone know where you're going, the route you'll take, and when you should return.
4. Carry a first aid kit and extra drinking water.
5. If you collect on dumps of abandoned mines, DO NOT, under any circumstances, enter shafts, and always be cautious when exploring the surrounding regions. There are often hidden tunnels, rotted ground and pits, as well as rusty nails, broken glass and discarded chemicals; all of which create a potential hazard.
6. Respect property. Leave gates in the position they were found. Observe no trespassing signs. By respecting property, you'll preserve rockhounding accessibility for everyone.
7. Use "outdoor" sense. Watch the weather. Lightning storms and flash floods are common to Utah. Completely extinguish all fires. Do not litter. Be mindful of livestock and wildlife. Do not leave children and pets unattended. And if a situation looks dangerous, assume it is.
8. Be aware that Utah miners take their claims seriously. Claims are defended. Please do not trespass on a marked claim.

UTAH CLUBS & ORGANIZATIONS

For collecting Utah rocks and minerals with a group, sharing collecting tips, and displaying great finds, contact one of the following clubs.

Beehive Rock & Gem Club
P.O. Box 1011
Ogden, UT 84402

Cache Geological & Archeological Society
P.O. Box 411
Logan, UT 84323-0411

Color Country Gem & Mineral Society
P.O. Box 769
Panguitch, UT 84759

Golden Spike Gem & Mineral Society
1518 Canyon Road
Ogden, UT 84404

Mineral Collectors of Utah
C/O Rick Dalrymple
1955 North Redwood Road
Salt Lake City, UT 84116

Moab Points & Pebbles Rock Club
201 Walnut Lane
Box 31-15
Moab, UT 84532

Timpanogas Gem & Mineral Society
P.O. Box 65
Provo, UT 84601

Tooele Gem & Mineral Society
P.O. Box 348
Tooele, UT 84074

Utah Federation of Gem & Mineralogical Societies
1223 North 1500 West
Salt Lake City, UT 84116

Wasatch Gem & Mineral Society
P.O. Box 26491
Salt Lake City, UT 84126-0491

NATURAL HISTORY & MINING MUSEUMS

See some wonderful displays of rocks, minerals, mining artifacts, dinosaur skeletons, and other remnants of the Old West in Utah's museums.

Bingham Canyon Mine
   Visitor's Center
Bingham Canyon
(801) 322-7300

Prehistoric Museum
The College of Eastern Utah
155 East Main, Price
(801) 637-5060

Dinosaur National Monument
Jensen
(970) 374-3000

Earth Science Museum
Brigham Young University
1683 North Provo Canyon Road
(across from Cougar Stadium), Provo
(801) 378-2232

Hutching's Museum of Natural
   History
685 North Center, Lehi
(801) 768-7180

Iron Mission State Park & Museum
595 North Main, Cedar City
(801) 586-9290

Museum of Natural History
President's Circle, 1350 East
between 200 and 300 South
University of Utah, Salt Lake City
(801) 581-4303

Natural History Museum
Weber State University
Main Floor, Circular Lind
Lecture Hall, Ogden
(801) 626-6160

Natural History Museum
Southern Utah State University,
Cedar City
(801) 586-7000

Park City Museum
528 Main Street, Park City
(801) 649-6104

Park City Silver Mine Adventure
P.O. Box 3178
Park City, UT 84060
(801) 655-7444

Tooele County Museum
Between Third East and Broadway,
Tooele
(801) 882-2836 or 882-3195

Tintic Mining Museum
Eureka
(801) 433-6842

Union Station Natural History
   Museum
25th and Wall Ave., Ogden
(801) 629-8444

Utah Field House of Natural
   History State Park
235 East Main, Vernal
(801) 789-3799

Western Mining & Railroad Museum
296 South Main, Helper
(801) 472-3009

Halite, the crystallized occurrence of salt, can often be quite beautiful. If large enough, the sometimes faintly colored cubes can make outstanding specimens for display in a mineral collection. There are a number of regions where exquisite halite crystals can be gathered and this location is certainly one of them. With the immense concentration of salt in the Great Salt Lake, the situation is perfect for crystallization, especially in regions of evaporation, or around submerged twigs and rocks.

The primary problem with collecting at the Great Salt Lake is accessibility, since much of the salt and other suspended minerals are being mined for commercial purposes. There is one area, however, that does offer fairly good access — Stansbury Island, which is actually a peninsula (except when the lake is high) situated about thirty-five miles west of Salt Lake City. To get there, take Interstate 80 to Exit 84, jog onto the only road leading north and you will soon find yourself traveling past some evaporation ponds. The ponds different colors are the result of suspended impurities, such as other minerals and various forms of salt-loving algae.

When in the area, DO NOT, under any circumstances, drive off-road, even if the ground appears to be firm. Much of the terrain is simply a weak crust of salt over water. The same warning applies to hiking onto regions of seemingly firm and dry salt. Be satisfied with what can be found at the edge of open evaporation areas, starting with those near the interstate, continuing, sporadically, to those near the tip of Stansbury Island.

Many of the rocks near the shore are covered with delicate little halite crystal clusters. The still damp specimens are extremely delicate and should be treated with the utmost of care. In fact, even after they dry, the little cubes and cauliflowers of halite remain fragile and should be stored in a dry location.

An evaporation pond on the Island

GREAT SALT LAKE

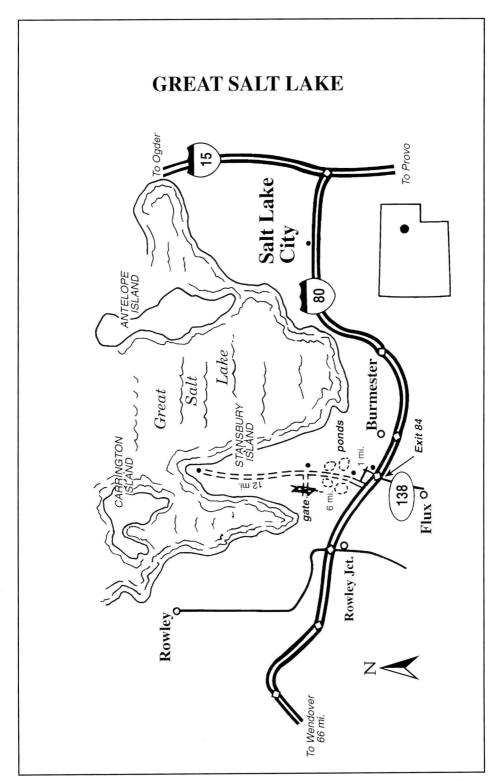

Outstanding specimens of fossilized trilobites, estimated to be over eighty million years old, can be found near Antelope Spring, about thirty-five miles west of Delta. Most of the fossil-bearing shale is protected by private claims, but collectors are allowed to dig in two of the most productive spots, as long as they get permission beforehand.

The first is owned by West Desert Collectors, 443 N. 350 E., in Delta, (810) 864-2175. It is necessary to first stop by their store to get travel and digging instructions, as well as permission to visit. The other spot is a fully staffed fee area called "You Dig Fossils," owned by the Bug House, 350 E. 300 S., also in Delta, (801) 864-2402. As you approach Antelope Springs, there are signs directing you to the fee area. The charge is minimal, especially when considering you will be allowed to work in productive areas and there will be someone there to assist you.

If you would prefer searching for trilobites on your own, off private claims, two other locations are presented on the accompanying map. They were not restricted at time of publication.

Whether you visit one of the private claims or you choose to explore Site A or Site B, you must first locate the fossil-bearing shale. It is easy to spot, due to its gray, blocky and layered appearance. In addition, there are usually tons of chips and debris directly below, created by previous rockhounds. After you have spotted a promising spot, it still takes a great deal of time, work, and patience to recover top quality fossils. Sizable portions of the shale must first be removed and then split as many times as necessary, in hopes that the newly exposed surfaces will contain undamaged trilobites. With care and practice you should be able to obtain some very fine specimens.

Trilobite in shale

DELTA

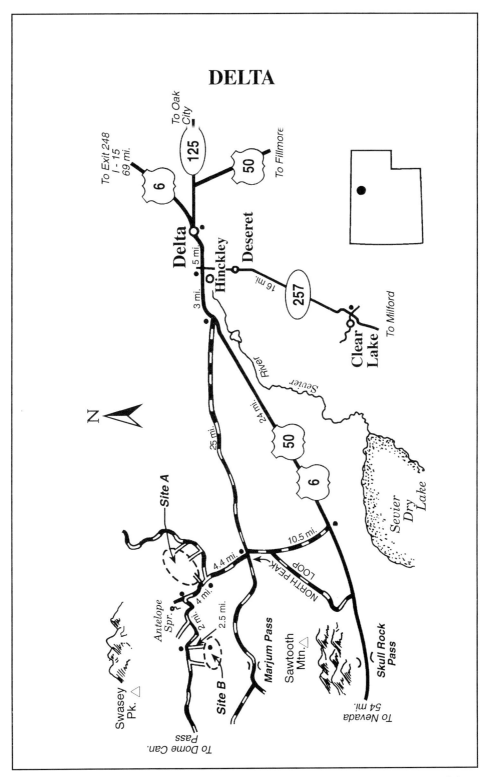

This location, situated only a few miles east of the Utah/Nevada border, provides rockhounds with good clean agate. To get there, take either Exit 2 or Exit 4 north from Interstate 80. Go about two miles toward Lucin, passing Danger Cave, as illustrated on the map. At that point, you will be near the southernmost portion of the Silver Island Mountains, which marks the edge of the site.

The best method for collecting here is to park and hike through the foothills east and northeast of the road. The terrain is fairly harsh, but there are random jeep tracks heading in all directions. If your vehicle has four-wheel drive and high clearance, you might want to go a little farther toward the mountains before stopping.

Most of the agate is white and uninteresting, but some does contain attractive inclusions and regions of pastel color. Carefully inspect everything you find, searching for areas that might produce good polished pieces. Agate is widely scattered thought the foothills, extending for a distance north and east.

A great amount of the easy-to-gather material has already been picked up, however, requiring more hiking through the rugged terrain in order to find much. Just be patient and willing to do some exploration and the trip will be worthwhile.

Supplies can be obtained in nearby Wendover. While in the area, be sure to visit the nearby Bonneville Salt Flats, home of so many land speed records.

Searching one of the numerous dumps

SILVER ISLAND MOUNTAINS

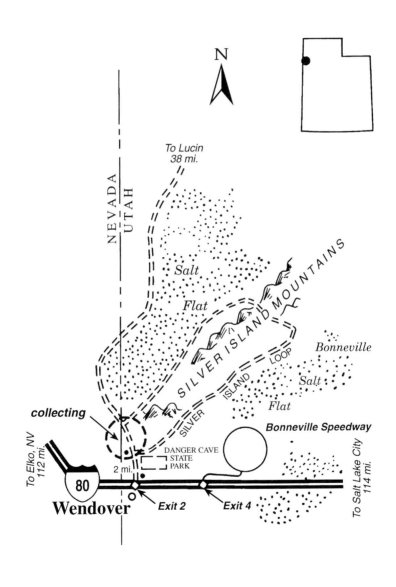

Painter Spring, situated in the west central part of the state, offers a variety of minerals for the collector. Go east from the Nevada/Utah border about twenty-five miles, on Highway 6/50, and then turn north, proceeding eight and six-tenths miles to a water tank. At the tank turn to the right, toward the mountains. From there, the road is not maintained and is washed out in places, making four-wheel drive advisable, if not necessary. Some rugged vehicles, however, should be able to make it all the way, if driven with caution.

Continue toward the scenic rock formations two more miles to Painter Spring, which is labeled Site A. Park near the spring and follow the faint trail leading up the hill through the trees and brush. As you hike, nice specimens of muscovite, pyrite, quartz, garnet, and pink feldspar can be found throughout the rocks and boulders on both sides of the trail. It takes some time and patience to find the best pieces, and most are small, but chunks containing more than one mineral make welcome additions to collections.

To get to Site B, go back to the very rough ruts leading south from the main road, as shown on the map. Proceed about one very bumpy mile to where additional minerals can be found. If you have time, it would probably be worthwhile to either drive or hike there. Be certain, however, that you and your vehicle are capable of this trip. Plenty can be found at the spring.

Be on the lookout for all types of animals, since the spring is a prime supplier of water for local wildlife. If you choose to camp here, do so a distance from the pools, so the animals will have unhindered access.

Site A

PAINTER SPRING

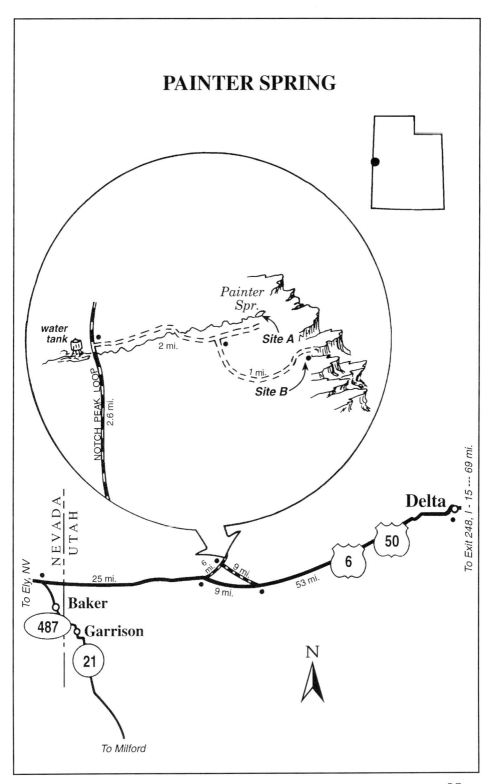

The area northeast of Eureka has long been known for its mineral production and many of the local copper and silver mines are still active. Of most interest to the hobbyist, however, is the large amount of very colorful agate, jasper, and opalite which can also be found throughout the region.

The jasper occurs in a variety of colors, including brown, gold and a prized red material filled with bright yellow swirls. There is also red jasper, inundated with white splotches, often referred to as "salami jasper." The agate is primarily found in shades of light brown, sometimes containing white inclusions, and the plastic-like opalite comes in the same hues as the jasper. Look for orange outcrops, which are often composed entirely of agate, jasper and/or opalite.

To get to Site A start at Tintic High School in town. Go east on Highway 6 three miles, and then turn north onto the rough old road. There is a stop sign and an unlocked gate, making it fairly easy to spot. Proceed about eight-tenths of a mile, park, and explore the hills in any direction, but primarily to the left. Site B is reached by continuing north about one-half mile more, and bearing right at the fork, as shown.

Sites C and D are accessed by returning to Highway 6, proceeding east another mile and one-half, and then turning onto the tough-to-spot ruts which lead through a gate into the hills on the left. Follow those ruts as they go around the hill, and, after traveling about one and one-tenth miles, you will drop into a canyon. Go to the bottom and then about half way up the opposite side to the center of Site C. Site D is about three-tenths of a mile farther up the road.

*Road to Site
A and B*

EUREKA

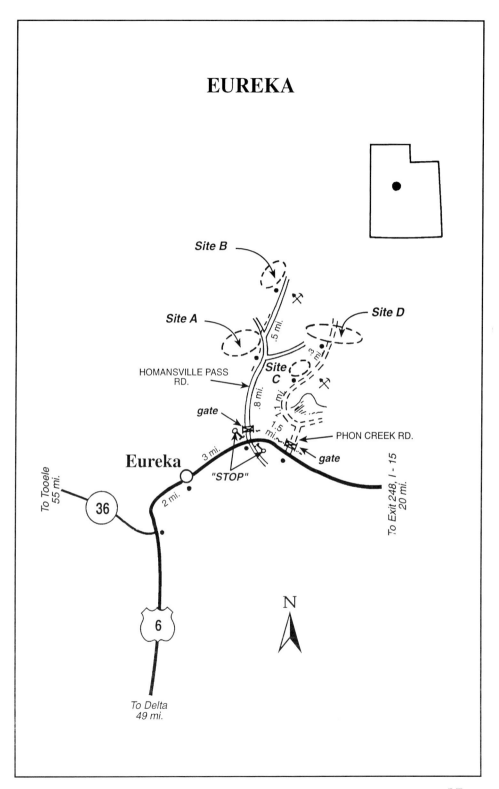

Site B

Site A

Site D

.5 mi.

HOMANSVILLE PASS RD.

Site C

.3 mi.

gate

.8 mi.

1.1 mi.

1.5 mi.

PHON CREEK RD.

Eureka

gate

3 mi.

"STOP"

To Tooele 55 mi.

36

2 mi.

To Exit 248, I - 15
20 mi.

N

6

To Delta
49 mi.

This is not a precise site, but, instead, an old mining region surrounding what used to be the town of Silver City. The list of what can be found within this once bustling mining area is lengthy and includes galena, pyrite, malachite, azurite, chrysocolla, quartz crystals, sphalerite, smithsonite, cerussite, limonite cubes, barite, and epidote. At one time, however, the minerals of prime interest were gold, silver, lead, zinc, and copper.

To get there, go south on Highway 6 about one and two-tenths miles from where Highway 36 intersects. At that point, there is a sign designating the turnoff to Silver City, and it is there where you should proceed east. Continue a little more than a mile to a fork, and you can either go left or right, since both directions will take you near numerous old dumps.

Be sure to allow enough time to do a good job of exploring this extensive area, since each of the old prospects tends to provide a unique offering of mineral diversity. Mines to the south tend to be quite different in mineral content than those to the north. In addition, better specimens are usually found either buried within the dump or in more inaccessible locations. Splitting large dump rocks will frequently expose otherwise concealed minerals and crystal pockets.

The primary caution here is to not forget that collecting status of old mines changes continuously, thereby making it mandatory for you to determine whether or not dumps you choose to explore are open to collecting. In addition, be sure to read the cautions presented in the Introduction about hazards associated with old mines.

Parked at the collecting site

SILVER CITY

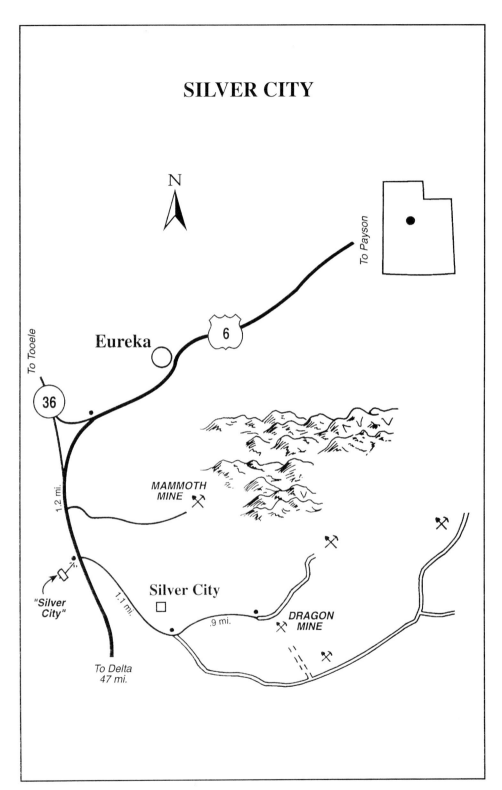

To Payson

N

Eureka

6

To Tooele

36

1.2 mi.

MAMMOTH MINE

"Silver City"

1.1 mi.

Silver City

To Delta 47 mi.

.9 mi.

DRAGON MINE

29

The rhyolite found at this location is very interesting. It is composed of little nodules which, when cut and polished, form concentric swirls or "eyes." The material comes in sizes up to huge boulders. In order to best display the unique patterning, make larger items with the collected material, such as bookends or spheres. Care should be taken to find only the best and most solid specimens, since much is cracked and/or pitted. Also be sure to pick up a few of the individual orbicular "eyes" which have weathered loose, since they can be quite interesting when sawed in half.

The collecting site is reached by taking the Yuba Lake turnoff (Exit 202) from Interstate 15, which is about twenty miles south of Nephi. After going two miles, ruts can be seen leading off to the right and it is there where you should turn and proceed into the red hills. This last stretch is somewhat rough, and if you are not sure your vehicle is capable of such a challenge, simply park well off the main road and walk the short distance. Small pieces of the fascinating rhyolite will be encountered the moment you leave the pavement, but larger and more compactly cemented material is situated in and around the main deposit, about two-tenths of a mile farther along.

Follow the bubbly rhyolite chips and chunks from regions near the road up to their primary source. Most of the climbs are not too steep, so getting to portions of the deposit is not difficult, but the footing is frequently unstable. Good material can be gathered at lower elevations if you are not in the mood for climbing.

The dirt road leading to the site

YUBA LAKE

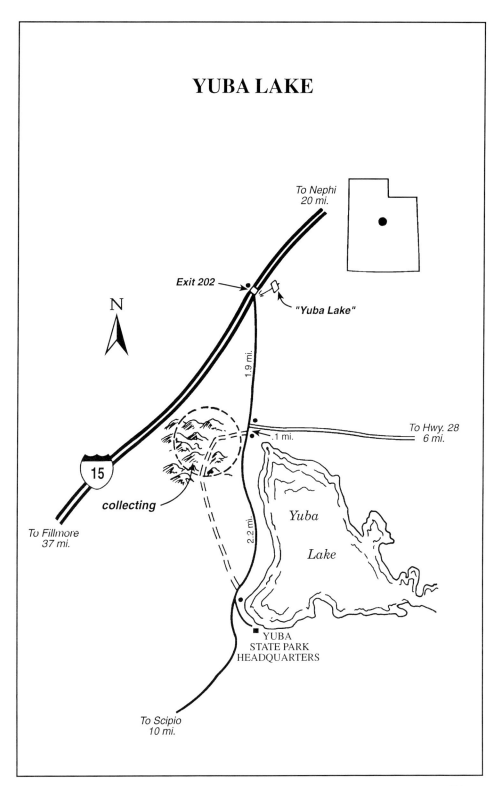

To Nephi
20 mi.

Exit 202

"Yuba Lake"

N

1.9 mi.

To Hwy. 28
6 mi.

.1 mi.

15

collecting

2.2 mi.

Yuba

Lake

To Fillmore
37 mi.

YUBA
STATE PARK
HEADQUARTERS

To Scipio
10 mi.

Until about ten years ago, both Ophir and Mercur were ghost towns and most dumps in the region were abandoned. Mercur, however, after nearly forty years of being idle, was reactivated by the Barrick Gold Mining Company, and is thereby closed to collectors. At time of publication, there was an interesting visitor center at the Barrick Mine, open five days a week (closed on Tuesdays and Wednesdays), from 10:00 A.M. until 7:00 P.M. Tours are conducted hourly and spending some time there is recommended.

To the northwest, near Ophir, there are still some productive and abandoned prospects open to collectors. It seems that the best spots are on the opposite side of the mountain, to the northwest. Getting there requires following the sometimes rough and steep road, as shown on the map. Four-wheel drive is probably not necessary, unless it is wet, but a good rugged vehicle is highly recommended. The drive offers spectacular views and passes lots of old mines as it heads up the hill.

If you don't want to tackle the mountain, there are some fairly productive dumps situated alongside the main road, starting only two-tenths of a mile from the highway and continuing through town. A few people still live in Ophir and additional information can probably be obtained there.

Included in the long list of minerals which can be found near Ophir are calcite, quartz, pyrite, white fluorite, realgar, cinnabar, and even some fossils. In order to find the best specimens, it is necessary to do a little digging into the dump. Split any suspect rocks in order to present an unweathered surface for evaluation.

Be certain not to trespass onto a private claim while collecting. Because of the work being done at Mercur, interest has returned to the region and a dump that is abandoned today may not be abandoned tomorrow.

Road to the Ophir sites

Examining a suspect rock near Ophir

OPHIR AND MERCUR

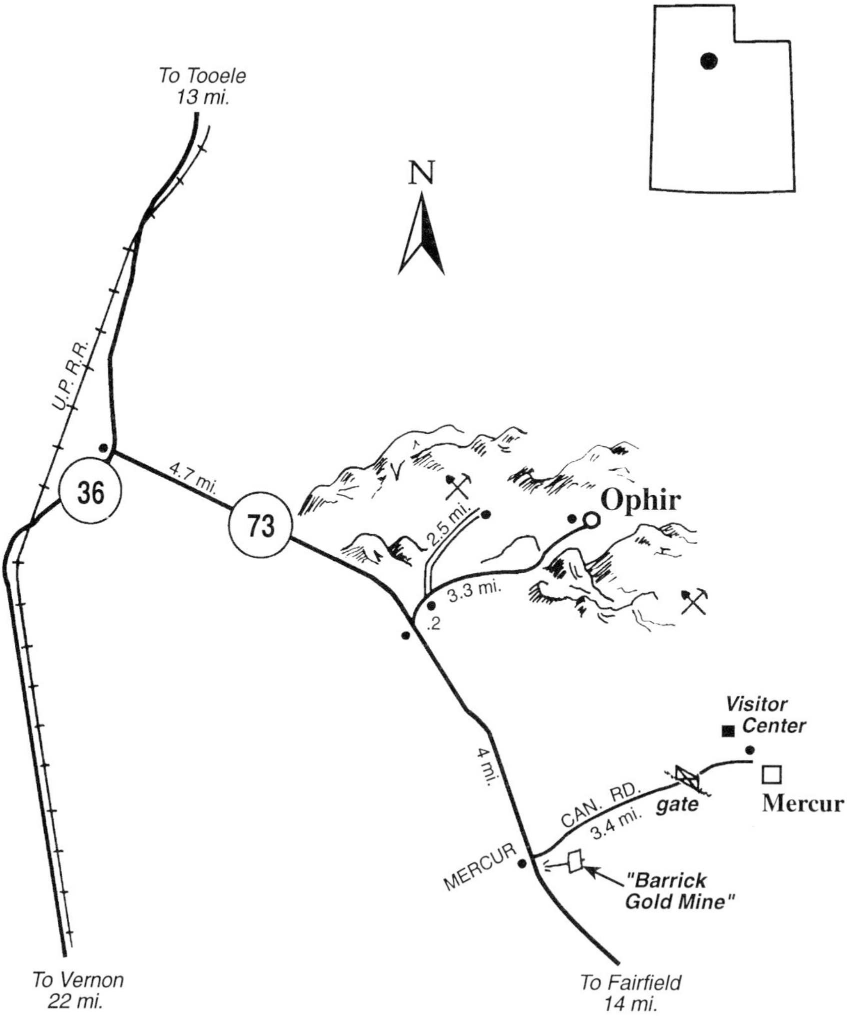

To Tooele
13 mi.

N

U.P.R.R.

36

73

4.7 mi.

2.5 mi.

Ophir

3.3 mi.

.2

4 mi.

Visitor
Center

Mercur

CAN. RD.

3.4 mi. gate

MERCUR

"Barrick
Gold Mine"

To Vernon
22 mi.

To Fairfield
14 mi.

These two sites are somewhat remote and the final stretch to both is rough. If the road is dry, four-wheel drive is probably not essential but it is desirable. Both sites are on BLM land, but you must go through private property to get there, so please respect the rights and requests of the land-owners as you pass through.

Site A features colorful jasper. To get there, carefully follow the instructions on the accompanying map, being certain that all range gates are left exactly as you find them. The small pump house, encountered as you approach the given mileage, is the landmark for Site A. Park about one-tenth of a mile past it and hike to the hills on the right.

Look for signs of where others have dug before. There are some small surface pebbles and chips of jasper to be found throughout the hills, but not much! Most must be obtained by heavy digging with a pick and shovel. The old excavations are tough to see from the road, since they have been partially and/or completely obscured by erosion over the years. Be willing to spend some time hiking in order to find clues. The jasper found at Site A is especially colorful, occurring in tones of yellow, gold, brown and red.

Site B is noted for its top quality petrified palm. To get there, follow the dim washed out ruts which intersect the "main" road approximately one-tenth of a mile before the pump house. Go about one mile up the hill, and

you should be able to see very faint signs of where previous collectors have been digging. It takes lots of pick and shovel work to find the wood, but the high quality helps make the work more bearable. Colors tend to be black, white and tan, but some nice green and red wood can also be found, either of which is a real prize.

Using a pick to dig for petrified palm at Site B

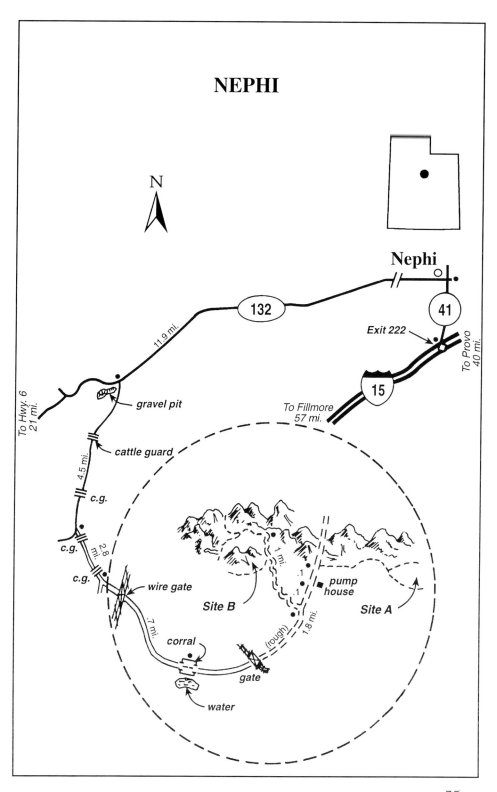

NEPHI

Topaz Mountain is definitely one of Utah's most famous gemstone collecting sites, boasting topaz crystals of a color and clarity that rival any to be found anywhere. A prized specimen to look for while in the area is a bixbyite crystal perched on a topaz crystal.

To get there, drive thirty-seven miles west from Highway 6 on Highway 174 to where a graded, dirt road intersects from the north. Follow that road two miles to the base of Topaz Mountain, labeled Site A on the map.

It takes time, patience, and work to find the elusive topaz, but the effort can be well rewarded. There are two productive methods for finding crystals. The first is to sift or screen the soil at the base of the mountain, hoping to find individual specimens that have weathered away from the host rock. The second is to attack the mountain itself with sledge hammers, chisels, picks, gads, and shovels, trying to break into a crystal-filled cavity. The mountain is open to digging with hand tools only and is currently closed to new mining claims. There are a few older claims which should be respected.

Be sure to visit the other two nearby collecting sites while in the area. Site B is reached by returning to Highway 174 and traveling west another six and one-half miles to where the pavement ends. From that point, all along the right fork, for quite a distance, the ground is covered with Apache tears. Most of the tears are black, but mahogany is also prevalent.

To reach Site C, double back four miles on Highway 174, and then turn south. After going about one mile, you can find jasper, agate, and rhyolite scattered on both sides of the road for at least another mile. The jasper is gold and yellow, while the agate occurs in a variety of different colors and patterns. A little walking from the road is required, but a respectable quantity can usually be picked up in a short amount of time.

Collecting Site A

TOPAZ MOUNTAIN

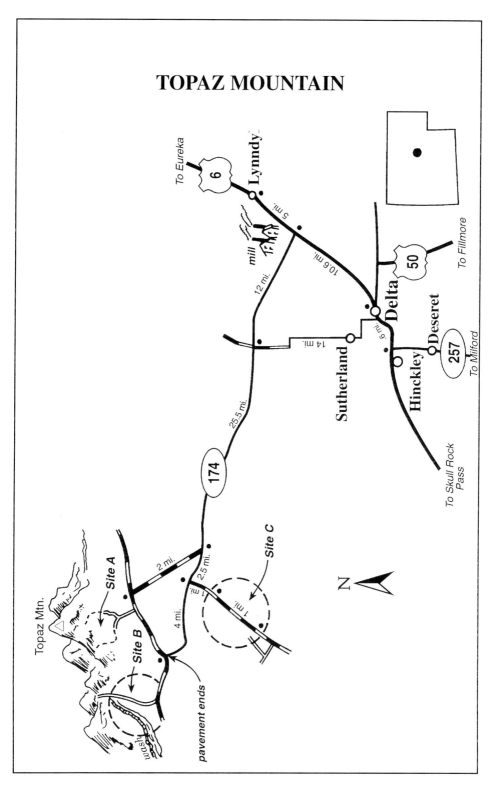

To Eureka

Lynndy

6

mill

5 mi.

10.6 mi.

12 mi.

50

To Fillmore

Delta

14 mi.

.9 mi.

Deseret

257

To Milford

Sutherland

Hinckley

25.5 mi.

174

To Skull Rock Pass

Topaz Mtn.

Site A

Site B

Site C

2 mi.

2.5 mi.

1 mi.

1 mi.

4 mi.

pavement ends

wash

N

Not far from Nephi, Utah, is a hill covered with high quality, banded, red and white onyx. Most of the onyx is fine grained and capable of taking an excellent polish.

To reach this most productive location, go six miles east from Nephi, on Highway 132. At that point, a road leading to Mt. Nebo intersects from the left. Follow that road three and one-half miles to the Nebo Scenic Loop. Turn right and continue two-tenths of a mile farther to where ruts can be seen on the left, heading up the hill through the trees. That is what remains of the road to the now abandoned onyx quarry. Since it is not possible to drive all the way to the diggings anymore, you should park off the pavement and hike the relatively short distance.

To get the best specimens, be sure to take a sledge hammer, as well as gads, chisels, and pry bars, since the tough onyx must be broken loose from its place in the hill. Before starting work, though, be sure to spend a little time examining the entire deposit. Some portions offer considerably better material, in terms of color contrast, patterning, and density, than others. Also take time to survey the huge boulders at the base of the quarry, since, included in those colossal chunks of onyx, are regions of very nice material. Working the boulders is sometimes easier than attacking the side of the mountain, and your time and energy might be better spent.

If working the deposit with hard rock tools doesn't appeal to you, there are still plenty of smaller specimens to be found amongst the rubble at the base of the deposit and on the cliff below. If you want to spend the night, Ponderosa Campground, situated almost directly below the old quarry, offers a good place to do so.

Banded onyx

PONDEROSA CAMPGROUND

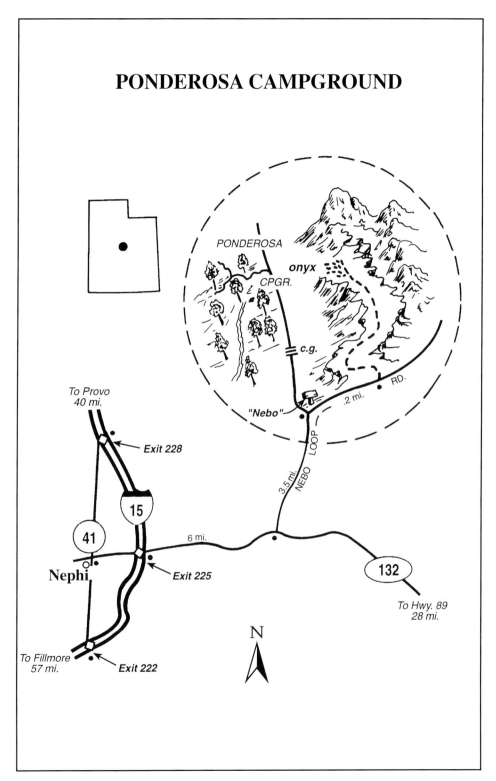

PONDEROSA

onyx

CPGR.

c.g.

RD.

.2 mi.

"Nebo"

To Provo
40 mi.

Exit 228

15

41

3.5 mi.

NEBO LOOP

6 mi.

Nephi

Exit 225

132

To Hwy. 89
28 mi.

To Fillmore
57 mi.

Exit 222

N

This location is somewhat remote, so extra water and food should be taken along, especially if traveling alone. The roads to the geode beds, for the most part, are in good shape, with some minor washouts along the way. Most rugged vehicles should have no trouble making the trip, unless there have been recent heavy rains.

At the collecting site, pits which have been left by previous rockhounds can be seen throughout the hills and valleys for quite a distance. To aid in deciding where you should start digging, it is sometimes helpful to examine the soil around many of those pits to ascertain what might have been found there. In fact, some very nice crystals and partial geodes can sometimes be obtained in that manner.

Once you have determined where to start, use a pick and shovel to dig two to five feet below the surface, being careful to examine all stones encountered. The geodes are fairly easy to spot since they tend to be spherical, and a good percentage contain fine agate and/or have prize crystal cavities. Some of the geodes may also contain chalcedony. Lots of them however, are duds, simply being solid, uninteresting balls of rhyolite. The only way to determine if what you have is worth keeping is to saw it in half, unless you only want hollows. In that case, relative weight is a good indicator. Obviously, the lighter the weight, the better chance it has of being hollow.

The digging is tough work, and the temperatures during the summer can soar to well over one hundred degrees. Since this is one of the country's premier collecting locations, those hardships are usually well compensated for with lots of beautiful crystal- and agate-filled geodes.

Sample of the type of geodes found at Dugway

DUGWAY

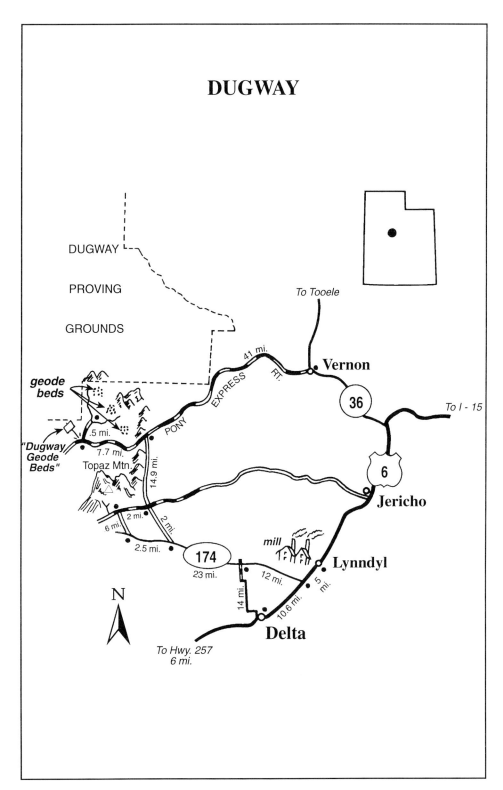

DUGWAY

PROVING

GROUNDS

geode beds

.5 mi.

7.7 mi.

Topaz Mtn.

14.9 mi.

"Dugway Geode Beds"

PONY EXPRESS Rt.

41 mi.

To Tooele

Vernon

36

To I - 15

6

Jericho

2 mi.

2 mi.

6 mi.

2.5 mi.

174

23 mi.

mill

12 mi.

Lynndyl

5 mi.

14 mi.

10.6 mi.

Delta

N

To Hwy. 257 6 mi.

This is one of the best places in Utah to obtain wonderstone, a colorful swirled variety of rhyolite. To reach the digging area, proceed two miles west from Eureka on Highway 6 and then north on Highway 36, approximately seventeen additional miles, toward Vernon and Tooele. At that point, turn right onto the ruts just past the railroad tracks. Wonderstone can be found throughout the hills north of the tracks, but there is one area, in particular, which is especially good. That spot is reached by paralleling the tracks one and seven-tenths miles, and then bearing left another four-tenths of a mile to the mounds. Watch for claims before working.

On the shallow ridge a few yards north of the mounds, are the wonderstone seams. Be warned that it will take some hard work with sledge hammer, chisels and gads to extract the tough rhyolite from its place in the host rock. In fact, you will probably have to break up some of the encasing material in order to attain a good enough angle of attack to remove sufficiently large chunks. If you don't want to go to all that work, there is plenty to be found in the mounds, but it tends to be small.

Some of the wonderstone is porous, so take enough time to obtain only the best. If you have some pieces with exceptionally good banding, but they are too grainy for polishing, try spraying with clear acrylic to enhance the colors and patterns.

Hills at the collecting site

VERNON

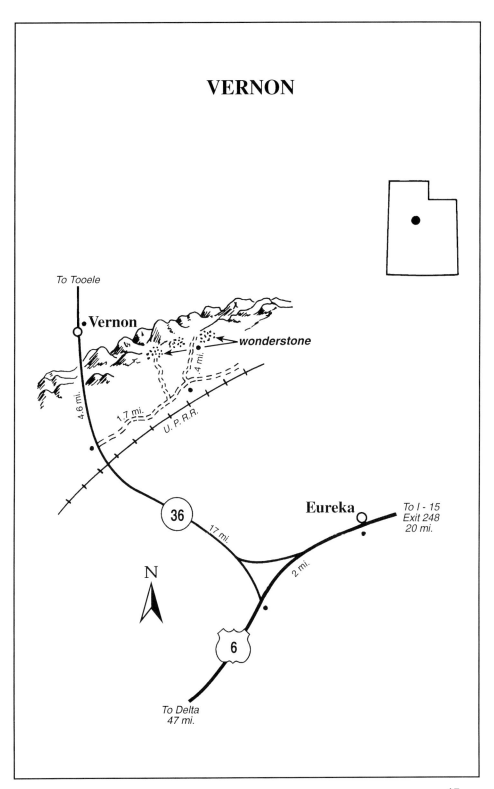

To Tooele

Vernon

wonderstone

4.6 mi.

1.7 mi.

1-4 mi.

U. P. R.R.

36

17 mi.

Eureka

To I - 15
Exit 248
20 mi.

2 mi.

N

6

To Delta
47 mi.

Fossilized red horn coral can be obtained a few miles northeast of Heber City, but access to the location requires an uphill hike of about one and one-half miles. If you are still interested, start in Francis and drive three and nine-tenths miles southeast out of town, on Highway 35, to the Woodland Store. From there, continue two more miles to where traces of an old road can be seen going up the hill through the trees and overgrowth on the left. This was once Riley Canyon Road, but it was closed by the Forest Service a number of years ago. Unless the Forest Service decides to reopen it, which seems unlikely, it is now necessary to park off the pavement and hike from that point.

Approximately one-half mile into the canyon there is a fork, and you should bear left, staying on what is left of the main road as it winds its way over the ridge. At the crest, a little more than a mile from the fork, eroded pits and trenches (most of which are overgrown with brush and thereby difficult to spot) will be seen.

The horn coral is embedded in the limestone and is very difficult to find. At one time, there were some commercial claims here, and the highly-prized red coral was being actively "mined." Those deposits, however, ceased providing enough specimens to make the ventures profitable, and, one by one, they closed down, but scars left by their digging can still be seen.

Occasionally, a fragment of small coral can be found lying loose, but to get the finest, it is necessary to attack the fossil-bearing limestone, which is not an easy task! Use a sledge hammer and some pry bars to remove chunks, and then split them, in hopes of spotting some coral. The bright red specimens can be cut and polished to produce exquisite pieces, and complete, undamaged coral still partially embedded in the host rock is outstanding for display.

Be very careful not to get into a pit or trench which is over your head, since the seemingly strong limestone caves in from time to time, creating a very hazardous situation.

WOODLAND

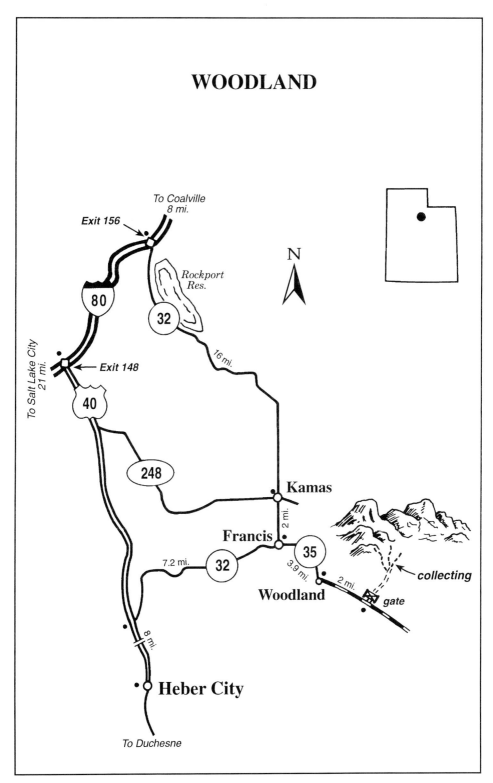

To Coalville
8 mi.

Exit 156

Rockport
Res.

80

32

N

To Salt Lake City
21 mi.

Exit 148

40

16 mi.

248

Kamas

2 mi.

Francis

32

35

7.2 mi.

3.9 mi.

collecting

2 mi.

Woodland

gate

8 mi.

Heber City

To Duchesne

The birdseye limestone found at this location is top quality and can be used to make beautiful spheres, bookends, and cabs. The drive to the collecting area is steep; but if the road is dry, most rugged vehicles should have no trouble. Go south from the ruins of Thistle Station, on Highway 89, four and three-tenths miles. At that point, on the east side of the highway, is a mailbox and a road going past it. Follow that road two-tenths of a mile to a fork, where you should bear right and start to climb the mountain. DO NOT go left onto the ranch.

As you leave private land the road becomes Forest Road 126. After going one and one-tenth miles, there is another fork. From that fork, and continuing along the right branch for at least one-half mile, one can find lots of "eye"-filled limestone alongside the road and among the trees on either side. The quality varies considerably, so be sure to take sufficient time to locate material with the most pronounced "eyes" and the best color contrast. Some specimens are more porous than others, so look for the most solid pieces. It isn't difficult to find good quality specimens in a relatively short amount of time from the cleared areas and along the road. Some of the limestone is partially or fully covered by pine needles and it may be necessary to use a grass rake to move the needles off underlying rock.

This is a beautiful forested location with many spectacular views along the road to the collecting site.

Collecting at the fork in the road

BIRDSEYE

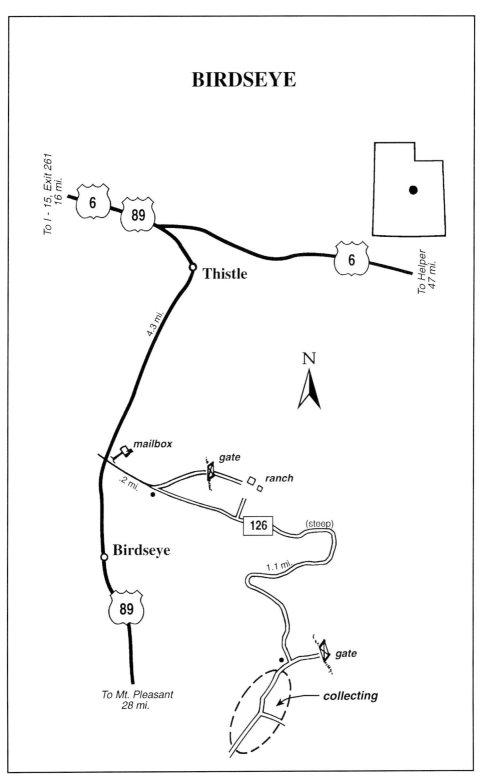

To I - 15, Exit 261
16 mi.

6 89

6

To Helper
47 mi.

Thistle

4.3 mi.

N

mailbox

gate

.2 mi.

ranch

126 (steep)

Birdseye

1.1 mi.

89

To Mt. Pleasant
28 mi.

gate

collecting

Nice specimens of cutting-grade petrified wood can be found at this location, but, unless you are very lucky, digging will be required. To get there, take Interstate 80 about twenty-two miles east from Salt Lake City, to where Highway 40/189 intersects. Drive south one mile to the Silver Summit offramp, Exit 2, and cross east over the highway toward the large building.

After going only one-tenth of a mile from the bridge, proceed left onto the dirt road one and six-tenths miles, as it heads back toward and then parallels the interstate. At that point, there is a sign designating the turnoff to the Silver Creek Wastewater Treatment Plant, and you should go right two-tenths of a mile, and then right again onto the dim ruts leading to the west. Go one more mile, passing under the power lines, and park. This location is on private land, but, at time of publication, the landowners did not object to rockhounds collecting, as long as the digging pits were refilled. If there are indications that status may have changed, do not trespass!

From where you park, the primary collecting area is north of the road, but it is very overgrown and difficult to spot without walking around. Look for soft soil as a good indicator of where previous collectors have been digging. You should be able to spot some small chunks and chips of the wood lying on the surface among the brush. The best, however, is obtained by digging. It will be necessary to use a sturdy pick and shovel to loosen the

clay, and a rock pick to bust up clods, after being removed, in order to check for included wood. If the soil is wet, the clay forms a gummy mess and the digging is even more challenging.

Once the wood is freed, it still must be rinsed in order to accurately ascertain its desirability. Colors tend toward brown, black, gold, yellow and a most pleasing honey hue. Some specimens contain red, white and/or black streaks and such pieces often take a fine polish.

Getting a closer look at a specimen

SILVER CREEK JUNCTION

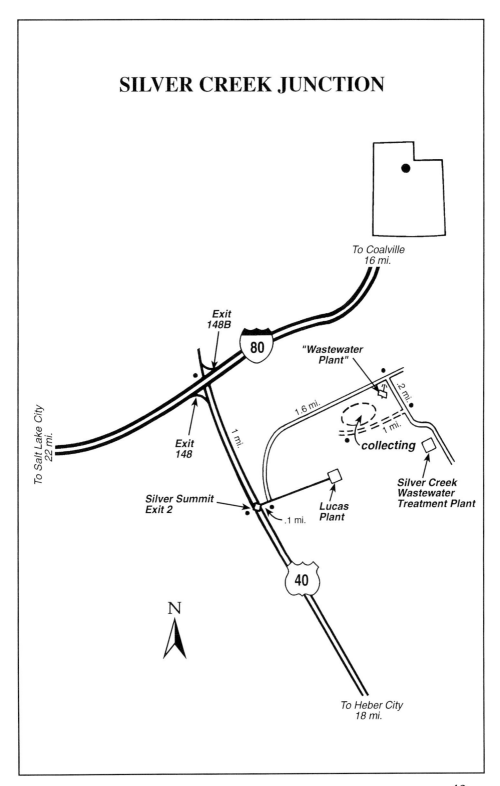

To Coalville
16 mi.

Exit
148B

80

"Wastewater
Plant"

1.6 mi.

.2 mi.

1 mi.

collecting

Exit
148

To Salt Lake City
22 mi.

1 mi.

Silver Creek
Wastewater
Treatment Plant

Silver Summit
Exit 2

Lucas
Plant

.1 mi.

40

N

To Heber City
18 mi.

Septarium nodules are highly prized by collectors and can be found in museums and mineral shops throughout the world. Some of the finest such nodules are found in Utah, but, because of their value, most deposits are protected by private claims. In addition, even if the claims didn't exist, they are usually found well below the surface, making it necessary to use bull-dozers and other heavy equipment to get to them. There is one place, near Alton, where the nodules occur nearer the surface, but are too randomly scattered to make commercial mining profitable.

To get there, go east from Alton on Forest Road 087, as shown on the map. Drive only two-tenths of a mile and then turn right onto the well-graded road going south. One and four-tenths miles farther along another well-traveled road intersects on the right. It is there where you should again turn, proceeding a little more than five miles to the edge of a large wash. Be sure to leave all range gates exactly as they were found. Along the way, two old coal mines will be passed, and a stop at either of them might produce a few interesting specimens.

At the given mileage, you will be heading down a forested hill, which is the start of the collecting area. Terrain in all directions from the road, on either side of the large wash, afford good places to search for the elusive septarium nodules. Broken ones will be spotted on the surface, and, from time to time, even complete specimens can be discovered, especially in and

near the wash and other areas of erosion. In any event, it is usually neces-sary to dig with pick and shovel for the best speci-mens. There is no par-ticular spot to start. Look for surface fragments or pits made by previous collectors for a clue, and be willing to spend some time and energy.

Gathering nodules

LONG VALLEY JUNCTION

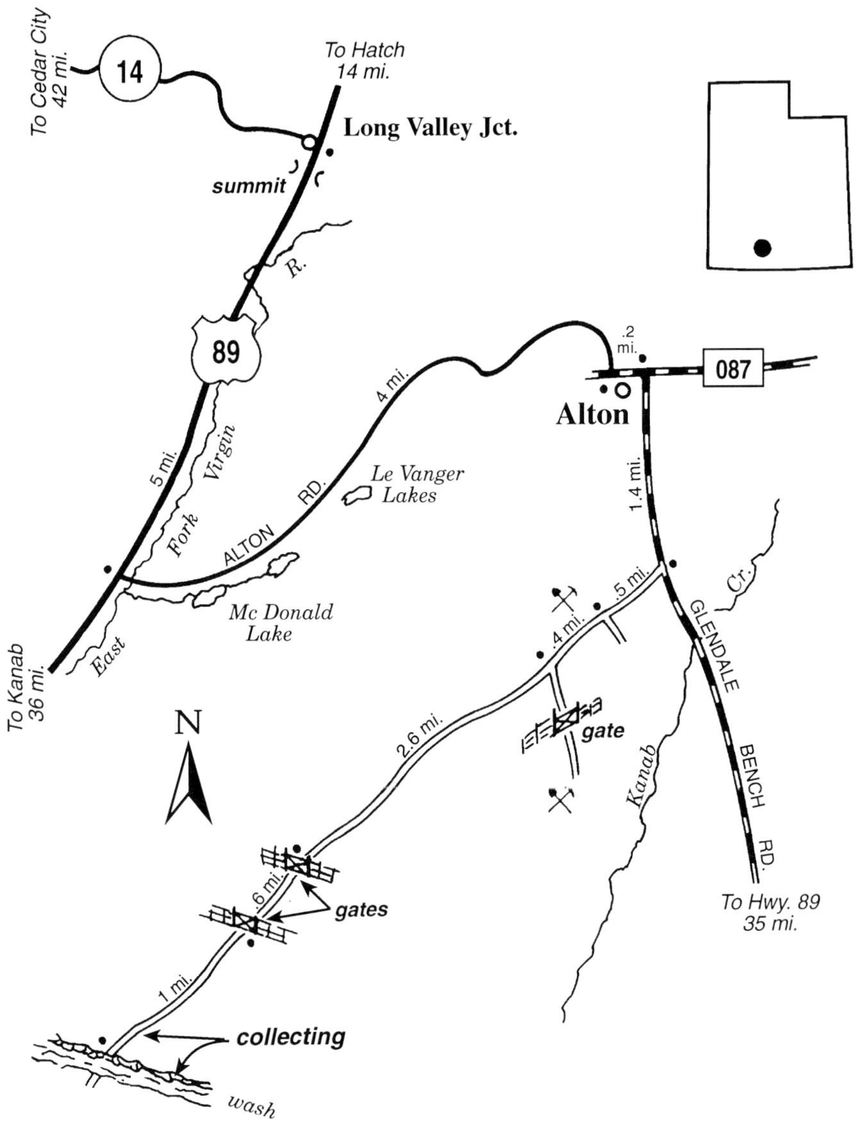

To Cedar City
42 mi.

14

To Hatch
14 mi.

Long Valley Jct.

summit

R.

89

4 mi.

.2 mi.

087

Alton

5 mi.

Virgin

Fork

ALTON RD.

Le Vanger
Lakes

1.4 mi.

Mc Donald
Lake

.5 mi.

4 mi.

To Kanab
36 mi.

East

N

2.6 mi.

gate

GLENDALE

Cr.

Kanab

BENCH RD.

.6 mi.

gates

To Hwy. 89
35 mi.

1 mi.

collecting

wash

These four collecting sites, situated in a very scenic portion of the state, afford the opportunity to gather fine specimens of petrified wood and fossils. To get to the first, labeled Site A on the accompanying map, take the graded, dirt road leading south from Cannonville to Grosvenors Arch, which is about an eighteen mile drive on well-graded dirt roads.

Petrified wood can be found scattered throughout the cliffs and washes surrounding the arch, but the greatest concentrations seem to be behind it. There isn't a lot left, and it will take some time and patient searching to find much, but what can be picked up is nice. The spectacular 152-foot high sandstone bridge was named in honor of Dr. Gilbert Grosvenor, founder of the National Geographic Society, and just seeing it is worth making the trip, even if there was no collecting in the vicinity.

At Sites B, C, and D, fossilized pelecypods and gastropods occur in the shale which can be seen crumbling down the slopes at each location. As was the case with Site A, they, too, do not provide easy-to-find specimens. To get the elusive fossils, it is necessary to patiently split the shale and carefully examine freshly exposed surfaces for traces of the prehistoric sea life. Once something is found, careful work with a small chisel, knife, and/or ice pick will help to expose the entire fossil(s). The work isn't difficult, but it does take some time and persistence to properly extract the best these sites have to offer.

If you have a rugged four-wheel drive vehicle and a sense of adventure, continue south along the road to Old Paria, where beautiful red petrified wood can be found throughout the hills and washes. The road is very rough and sandy past Cottonwood Canyon, though, so don't venture in unless you are sure you can make it!

Collecting at Site A

KODACHROME BASIN

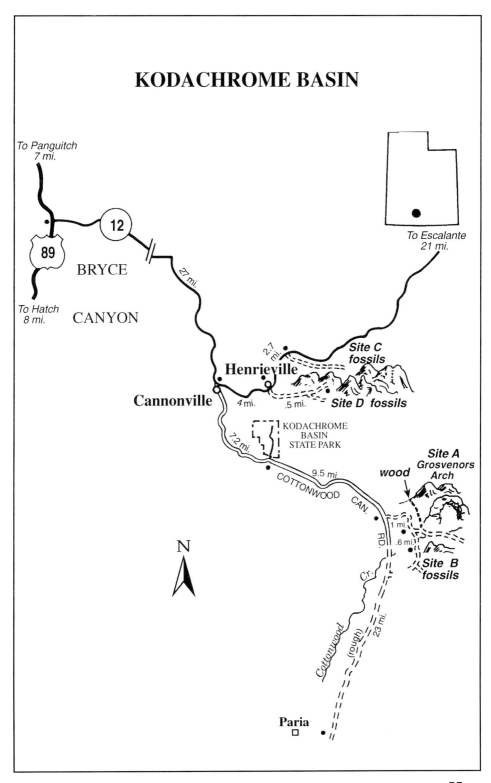

To Panguitch
7 mi.

To Hatch
8 mi.

89

12

BRYCE

CANYON

27 mi.

To Escalante
21 mi.

Henrieville

Cannonville

2.7 mi.

Site C
fossils

4 mi.

.5 mi.

Site D fossils

KODACHROME
BASIN
STATE PARK

7.2 mi.

COTTONWOOD CAN.

9.5 mi.

wood

Site A
Grosvenors
Arch

1 mi.

.6 mi.

Site B
fossils

N

COTTONWOOD CAN. RD.

Cottonwood Cr.

(rough)

23 mi.

Paria

53

Petrified wood can be found in outcrops near the town of Hurricane. Most of the outcrops, however, are difficult to get to, but one spot, situated on Little Creek Mountain, is quite accessible. To get there, take Highway 59 thirteen miles east from Hurricane and then go south eight-tenths of a mile on the easily-spotted, graded, dirt road. At that point there is a fork where you should bear right another two miles. The road is rough in places, especially as it climbs onto the mesa, but most vehicles should have no trouble if driven with care.

At the given mileage, you will be on a tree covered mesa, and, extending for quite a distance, petrified wood can be found in random concentrations. Most of the surface pieces are not very large, but complete logs have been discovered. The site has been known for many years, so your best chance for finding big specimens is to pay particularly close attention to areas of erosion. Look for partially exposed chunks, and then dig out what is buried. Sometimes that buried portion will have colossal proportions. In addition, do not hesitate to spend some time walking away from the road, since better material always seems to be more abundant in more difficult to get to locations. Just don't lose your bearings.

Much of the wood is tan and filled with pits, which makes polishing impractical, but nice brown, yellow, red, orange and black gem material can

also be obtained. Be sure to allow sufficient time for adequate exploration of the area. Even the porous material, however, is still nice for display.

Gathering specimens at the collecting area

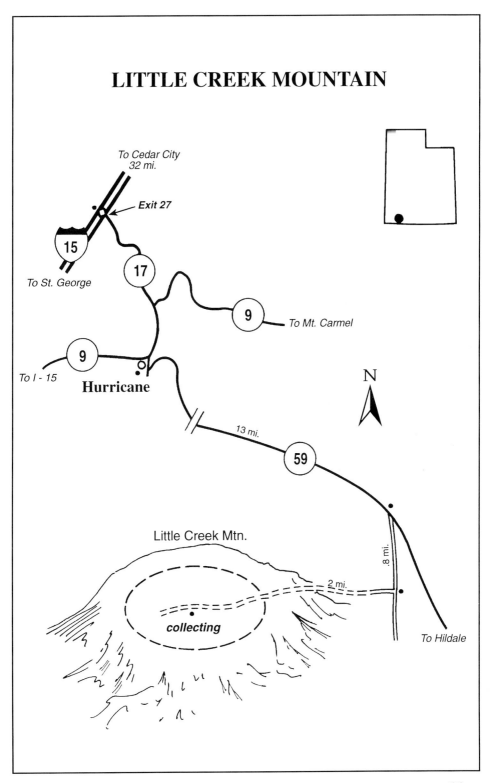

LITTLE CREEK MOUNTAIN

To Cedar City
32 mi.

Exit 27

15

To St. George

17

9

To Mt. Carmel

9

To I - 15

Hurricane

13 mi.

59

N

Little Creek Mtn.

.8 mi.

2 mi.

collecting

To Hildale

This is truly a bountiful agate field, extending many miles throughout the foothills east of Interstate 15 between Summit and Cedar City. Simply follow any of the ruts leading from the access road, as shown on the map. Go about one-half mile to where the collecting starts, and, from there, continue as far as you like into the hills. Agate is scattered throughout the terrain for quite a distance, but the concentration does vary. If you are unsatisfied with one spot, drive a little farther and try again.

An incredible variety of hues and patterns can be found, and it seems that each place has something slightly different to offer. The colors range from brilliant red, orange, and blue to darker shades of rust, gold, and black. It is not uncommon to find plume and dendrite material, as well as that displaying fine patchwork patterns. Size ranges from very small chips to huge boulders, and the quality is remarkably good, even in the larger specimens.

Access to the Fiddlers Canyon location, just north of Cedar City, is still available, at time of publication, but housing construction may soon change that status. Take Exit 62, from Interstate 15, go six-tenths of a mile to Fiddlers Canyon Road, and follow the pavement one and one-tenth miles to its end. From there, either take some of the tracks leading past the construction into the canyon or park and hike. Just be certain not to trespass. Good sized chunks of beautiful sky blue agate can be found in random concentrations. Pay particularly close attention to where road graders and tractors have been working, since the housing and road building project has unearthed tons of beautiful material.

The roads past the pavement are very rough, but if you have a rugged vehicle, and access is still available, try to get farther into the canyon.

End of the road at Fiddlers Canyon

SUMMIT

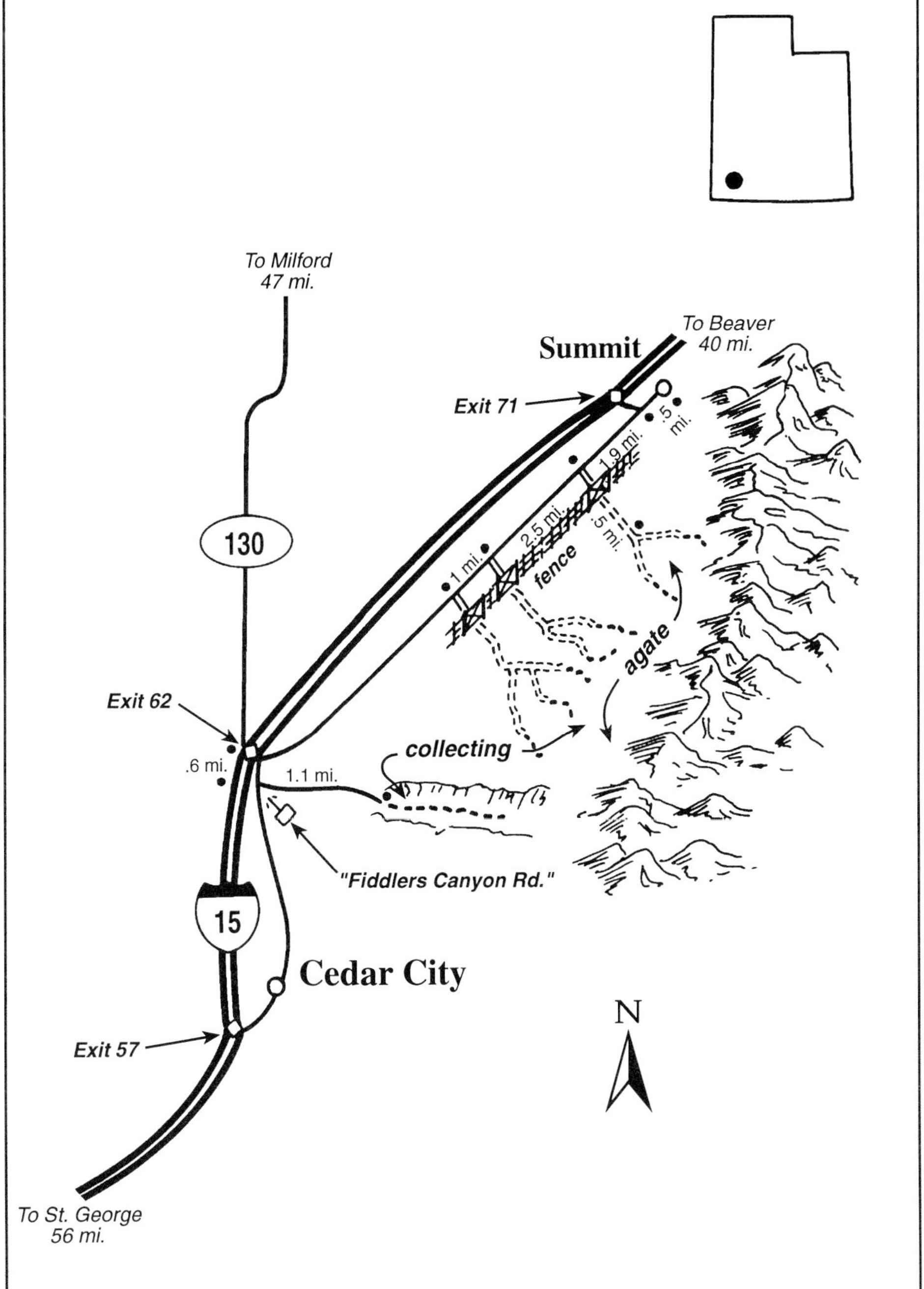

To Milford
47 mi.

To Beaver
40 mi.

Summit

Exit 71

• .5 mi.

1.9 mi.

2.5 mi.

.5 mi.

• 1 mi.

fence

agate

130

Exit 62

.6 mi.

1.1 mi.

collecting

"Fiddlers Canyon Rd."

15

Cedar City

N

Exit 57

To St. George
56 mi.

Agate, wonderstone, and conglomerate can be found at the two adjacent sites illustrated on the map. To get there, take Exit 71 from Interstate 15 and travel eight-tenths of a mile past Summit to a well-graded road leading off to the southeast, just before a large sign proclaiming the Cedar City / Parowan Range Rehabilitation Area. Take that road, cross the cattle guard, and go just under two miles to where a partially obscured auxiliary road intersects from the left. Proceed on the main route as it winds its way up the hill for another eight-tenths of a mile to Site A.

The drive to the collecting site affords numerous spectacular panoramas of the valley below. Those views help to make the trip even more enjoyable. Site A is tough to spot, as you round the corner, but it is composed of some tightly compacted chunks of pebble-filled conglomerate. Very little can be done with this interesting rock except using it for display, as is, since the cementing material seems far too porous for cutting and polishing. Some of the material is quite colorful and interesting. Look for pieces with the best color combinations and smallest pebbles.

Site B is only one-tenth of a mile farther along and features wonderstone (rhyolite). Much of the deposit, which is situated immediately adjacent to the road, is rather plain and it takes some time and effort to obtain chunks exhibiting bands or swirls with good color contrast. The material is hard, thereby requiring lots of work with sledge hammers, pry bars, and gads to break pieces from the primary, and somewhat small, deposit.

Higher on the hill, overlooking the wonderstone outcrops, and continuing into the little ravine on the opposite side, some nice chunks of agate can be picked up, primarily in shades of light blue, gray and white. There is some private land nearby, so be sure you do not trespass.

Removing material from Site B

PAROWAN

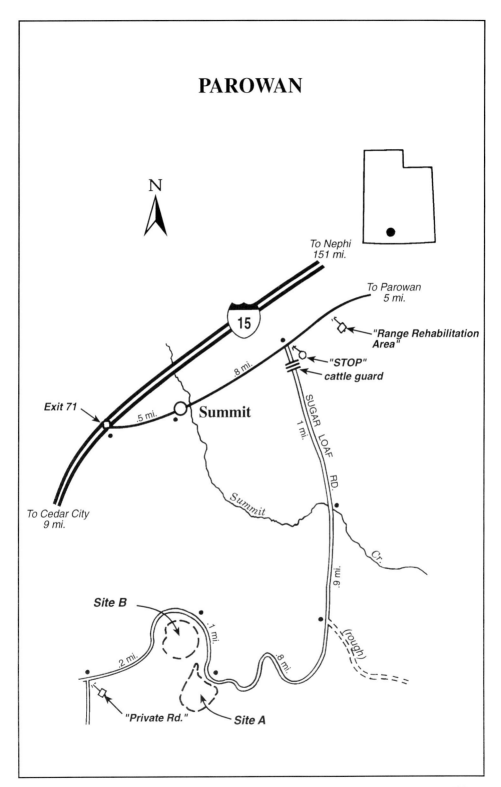

N

To Nephi
151 mi.

To Parowan
5 mi.

15

"Range Rehabilitation
Area"

"STOP"
cattle guard

.8 mi.

SUGAR LOAF RD.

1 mi.

Exit 71

.5 mi.

Summit

To Cedar City
9 mi.

Summit

Cr.

.9 mi.

Site B

.1 mi.

.2 mi.

(rough)

.8 mi.

"Private Rd."

Site A

The region in and around Brian Head is well known amongst skiers, but not many people are aware that lots of beautiful agate can also be found there. The two sites discussed here represent only small portions of the massive agate field which winds its way throughout the area, but they do provide a good sampling.

To get to Site A, go north one and four-tenths miles on Highway 143 from where it intersects Highway 148, as shown on the map. At that point, you will come to Forest Service Road 047, the route to Brian Head Peak. Proceed about four-tenths of a mile to Parowan Creek, which marks the start of the collecting area. Park anywhere from that point, extending all the way to the northern side of the mountain, and start looking. Search in all directions and pay particularly close attention to road cuts for the whitish agate. Don't be afraid to do some hiking, just pull off at a safe spot.

Colors range from a rather plain milky white material to some that is filled with red, orange, black and blue. Pieces displaying lots of color are obviously the most prized. Be advised that some of the Brian Head agate tends to be internally fractured. There is still plenty that isn't, just be patient and willing to spend some time searching.

Site B is reached by returning to Highway 143 and heading east four and seven-tenths miles from where Highway 148 intersects. At that point, there is a convenient little pull out on the south side of the road, and it is there where you should park. The collecting site is extensive and extends south from Highway 143 for quite a distance. Roam the hillside as it goes down to the river, looking for more agate in the same colors as those specimens found at Site A.

Site A

Site B

BRIAN HEAD

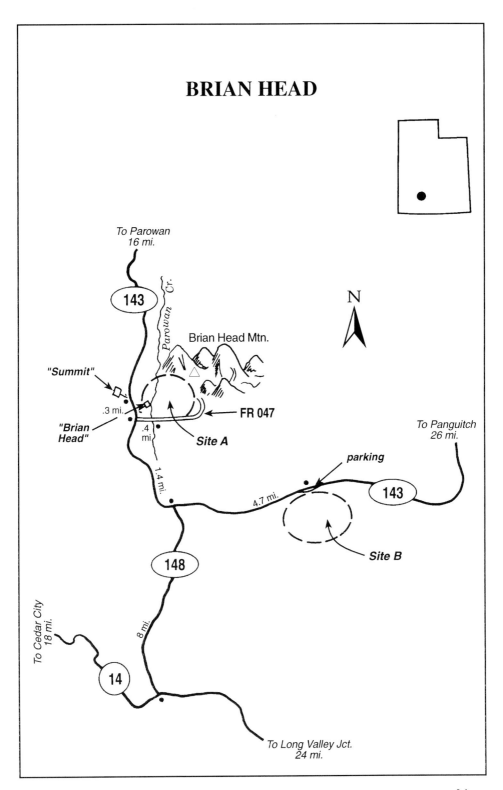

To Parowan
16 mi.

143

Parowan Cr.

Brian Head Mtn.

N

"Summit"

.3 mi.

"Brian
Head"

FR 047

.4
mi

Site A

To Panguitch
26 mi.

1.4 mi.

parking

4.7 mi.

143

148

Site B

To Cedar City
18 mi.

8 mi.

14

To Long Valley Jct.
24 mi.

This site is only a short distance south of Panguitch and features a tiny hill covered with a phenomenal variety of agate. In fact, just about every rock you will find on the hill is some type of agate, much of which is of good quality.

The turnoff is four and one-half miles south of Panguitch on Highway 89. Go east and proceed three and three-tenths miles on the fairly well-maintained, dirt road. You will pass through a range gate along the way. Be certain to close it after having passed through. A sandy wash is encountered at the two and one-half mile mark from the pavement, and it might present a problem for passenger cars. At the appropriate mileage, Agate Hill will be on the right. There is a good place to park on its eastern slopes, and the beautiful orange cliffs of Bryce Canyon can be seen in the distance.

The best collecting is on the hill itself, but additional material can be found scattered throughout the surrounding flatlands and in the extensive canyon farther east. All you must do is hike in just about any direction from Agate Hill and you will be able to spot lots of nice agate. Even though much of the agate is clean and solid, some is internally fractured. Take time to gather only the best, rather than haul home many pounds of marginal material. Much of the agate is clear with a multitude of different inclusions exhibiting dendritic, paisley and/or patchwork patterns. The most prized is the red and black material, which, as you might expect, is also the toughest to find. The parking area offers a great place to camp if you want to spend the night.

Gathering specimens at Agate Hill

AGATE HILL

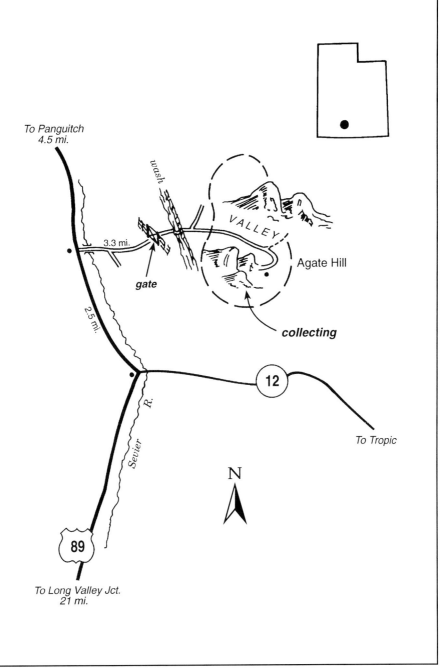

To Panguitch
4.5 mi.

wash

3.3 mi.

2.5 mi.

VALLEY

Agate Hill

gate

collecting

12

To Tropic

Sevier R.

89

N

To Long Valley Jct.
21 mi.

The region surrounding Panguitch is noted for its scenic beauty and the abundance of minerals that can be found there. This particular site consists of a series of washes a few miles north of town where rockhounds can find agate and jasper. The most prized are the agate nodules exhibiting beautiful red, yellow and green bands.

To get there, head north from Panguitch on Highway 89 to Sanford Creek Road, about eight miles from town. Turn east and proceed eight-tenths of a mile to the gravel pits. You cannot collect in the pits themselves, but areas of erosion surrounding the operation offer some potential. The primary wash, however, is six-tenths of a mile farther along.

This location has been known for quite a while, but, each year the rains seem to replenish the gemstone supply. Easily reached regions near the road tend to be less productive than spots a little farther away. Walk a distance through the main wash, in either direction, to other washes in the general area. Keep in mind that most of the rocks have a dull and abraded surface which makes them extremely difficult to identify. It is usually necessary to split all suspect stones in order to reveal their true identity. Be particularly suspicious of anything that displays even the slightest surface color.

If you don't find much by hiking this first wash, continue up the road and explore any of the others you might encounter for at least another mile. Strangely, very little can be found on the flatlands. Obviously, the agate and jasper come from a source upstream, and, if you have time, it might be fun to try to locate it.

Rockhounds can find agate and jasper throughout the wash

PANGUITCH

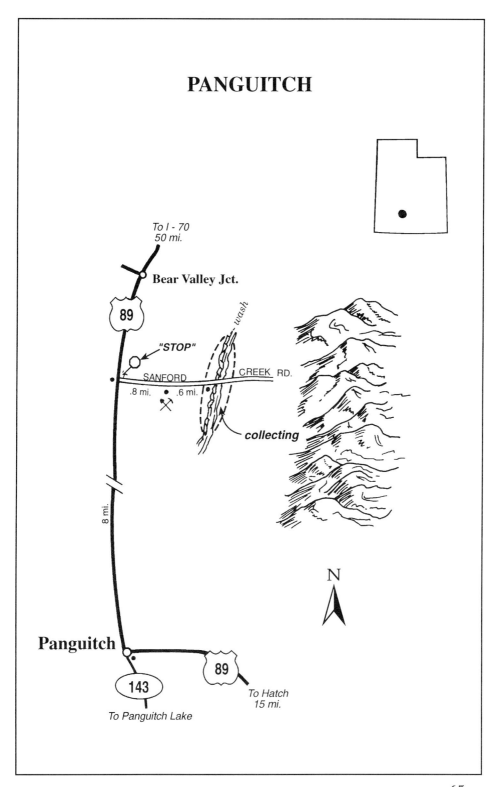

To I - 70
50 mi.

Bear Valley Jct.

89

"STOP"

SANFORD CREEK RD.

.8 mi. .6 mi.

wash

collecting

8 mi.

N

Panguitch

143

89

To Panguitch Lake

To Hatch
15 mi.

Agate and jasper, in a variety of colors and patterns, as well as chalcedony, obsidian, and rhyolite, can all be found at two locations only a short distance south of Beaver. The most prized mineral from this locality is a shimmering sky blue agate which can be used to produce exquisite cabochons and other polished pieces.

To reach the sites, take Exit 109 from Interstate 15. Go about one-tenth of a mile, and drive south onto the frontage road. Continue three-tenths of a mile, passing the large Camperland building, to where a dirt road intersects from the left. Turn there, proceed through the gates, being sure to securely reclose them, and travel one and one-half miles to a fork. Site A is accessed by going left another eight-tenths of a mile.

Explore the valley a short distance to the east as well as any regions of erosion for agate, jasper, obsidian, and rhyolite. Forested areas are difficult to inspect due to the thick layer of pine needles and leaves covering the ground, but raking them aside isn't hard and often helps to expose otherwise hidden minerals. Plan to do some walking, but be careful not to get lost. This collecting site has been known for years, and much of the easily found material has already been picked up.

To get to Site B, return to the fork and follow the very rough ruts leading off to the south. High-clearance, rugged vehicles are essential here, but four-wheel drive will probably not be needed. If you are not sure you can make it, park and hike the one and one-half miles. At the proper mileage, start looking for bright white chalcedony. Some is loose and easily spotted, but more frequently it is completely or partially embedded in the tightly compacted soil, requiring a screwdriver or pick and shovel to free it. Most of the "roses" are small, but they do tend to be well formed. Some are stained and may require cleaning when back home. Be sure to allow sufficient time to adequately explore this site, since the concentration varies considerably and the pine needles make discovery challenging.

BEAVER

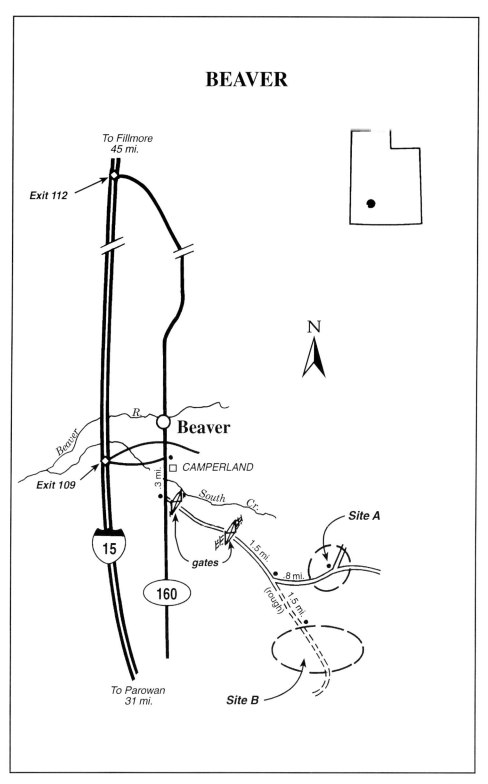

To Fillmore
45 mi.

Exit 112

N

R.

Beaver

Beaver

CAMPERLAND

Exit 109

.3 mi.

South *Cr.*

Site A

15

gates

1.5 mi.

.8 mi.

(rough) 1.5 mi.

160

To Parowan
31 mi.

Site B

This is one of those spots where collectors can actually find faceting-grade, gemstone crystals. The gem is labradorite, and the crystals can be found in sizes measuring up to one full inch in length, but most are no longer than one-quarter of an inch.

To get to this remarkable location, proceed south on Highway 257 thirteen and one-half miles from where it intersects Highway 6/50. At that point, some ruts will be seen leading east toward a tiny mountain only a short distance away. Follow those ruts one-half mile, as they go through a shallow pass, to the far side of the southernmost peak. This is the collecting area.

The labradorite crystallized in cavities of the andesite lava, which forms the knoll on top of the hill. To get the finest and largest crystals it is usually necessary to use a sledge hammer, gads, chisels and pry bars to break down the tough host rock, hoping to expose hidden cavities. Once a cavity is discovered, it is necessary to CAREFULLY work to fully open it and then examine the interior with the aid of a flashlight. Chances are very good that your flashlight beam will be greeted with sparkling little crystals.

Using hard rock tools to expose hidden gem-bearing cavities involves lots of time and hard work. By far, the easiest means of collecting is to simply pick crystals off the surrounding alkali flats which have been freed by the forces of nature. In the late afternoon and early morning the ground actually glistens because of the proliferation of labradorite crystals strewn throughout the landscape. Walk or, better yet, crawl, with the sun to your back and look for the sparkle. Hundreds of the tiny gems can be found in only a few hours by using this technique, and some of the specimens are as good as can be found within the freshly opened cavities.

Labradorite crystals gathered at the site

CLEAR LAKE

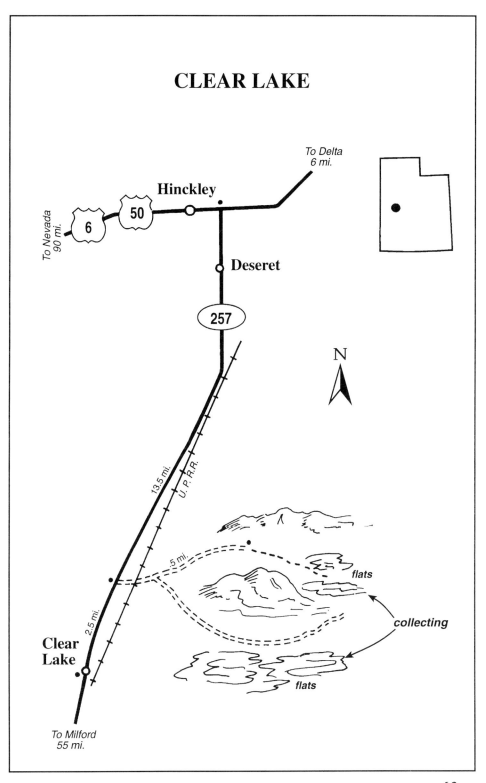

To Delta
6 mi.

Hinckley

To Nevada
90 mi.

6

50

Deseret

257

N

13.5 mi.

U. P. R.R.

.5 mi.

flats

collecting

2.5 mi.

Clear
Lake

flats

To Milford
55 mi.

The colorful Vermilion Cliffs around Kanab help to tell the story of what happened here during the Cretaceous Period. At that time, this once heavily forested region became buried by an inland sea. Trees were embedded in the silica rich mud and slowly petrified. The remnants of that ancient mud can be seen in the form of colorful mounds at the base of the cliffs, and it is in and around those areas where one can find beautiful jasper, agate and petrified wood.

The two collecting areas noted on the map are easily reached from Kanab, but much of the material near the roads has been depleted. With the constant process of wind and erosion, however, new material seems to be uncovered every season. There is still lots of incredibly beautiful agate, jasper and wood to be found throughout the entire region shown on the map. Hiking away from the more accessible areas is now the best way to assure success. To get to the prime sites, a rugged vehicle, preferably with four-wheel drive, will be required, due to the amount of loose sand that must be crossed.

Access to this most scenic collecting area is achieved by going east fifteen and four-tenths miles from Kanab, on Highway 89 to the turnoff. There is a sign posted just off the pavement warning travelers that the road is impassable when wet. That warning should be heeded, even if you have four-wheel drive. The soil is primarily clay, and, when wet, affords absolutely no traction.

You will encounter a gate, just after leaving the highway, and, after passing through, leave it exactly as it was. Continue through the sand, bearing toward the orange cliffs. When you have gone about three miles, there is a large wash which must be crossed. It may be necessary to do a little road repair here, since the banks can sometimes be very steep, especially if there have been recent heavy rainstorms.

The two sites shown on the map are productive, but following any of the many ruts heading off the main road toward the cliffs, will usually lead to other good locations.

View of Site A

VERMILION CLIFFS

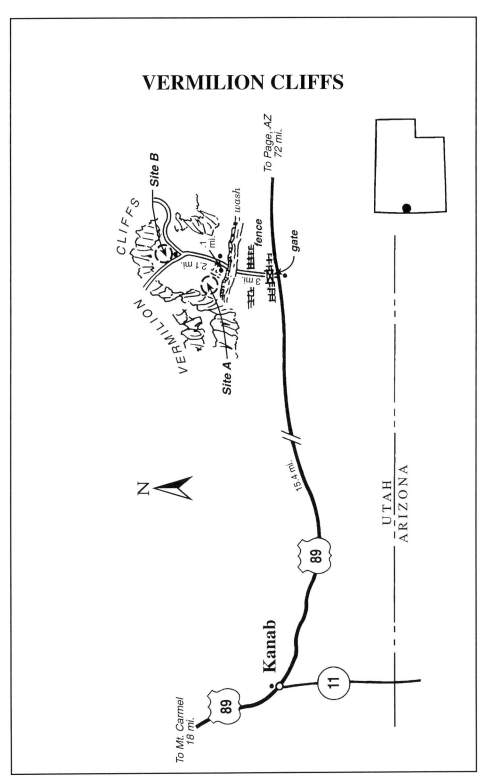

To Page, AZ
72 mi.

Site B

CLIFFS

wash

.1 mi.

2.1 mi.

fence

gate

.3 mi.

VERMILION

Site A

N

15.4 mi.

UTAH
ARIZONA

89

Kanab

11

To Mt. Carmel
18 mi.

89

Colorful agate, jasper, and petrified wood can be found scattered throughout the region shown on the map. Take Highway 89 twenty-eight miles east from Kanab. There, you will see a dirt road intersecting from the north, which should be followed. Go through the gate, leaving it just as you found it, and be on the lookout for rough spots. It might be necessary to move a few rocks and/or break down banks formed by heavy rainfall, and, because of that, four-wheel drive is highly recommended.

After traveling about one and one-half miles, you should begin finding material randomly scattered on both sides of the road, including pieces of the prize red agate which has made this location famous. The quantities vary considerably along the way but tend to get better as you proceed. The prime collecting is at the canyon overlook, seven and four-tenths miles from the highway. You should search the canyon slopes as well as the flatlands for quite a distance. Most surface material near the road has been depleted, so some hiking is probably necessary if you want to find much.

The flats at the canyon overlook mark the site of Old Paria, an entire frontier town built many years ago by the movie industry. Very little evidence of the old movie set remains there today, but such films as *Drums Along the Mohawk, Union Pacific, Red Canyon*, and *Death Valley Days* were filmed there because of the beautiful surroundings.

Prime collecting is at the canyon overlook

PARIA RIVER

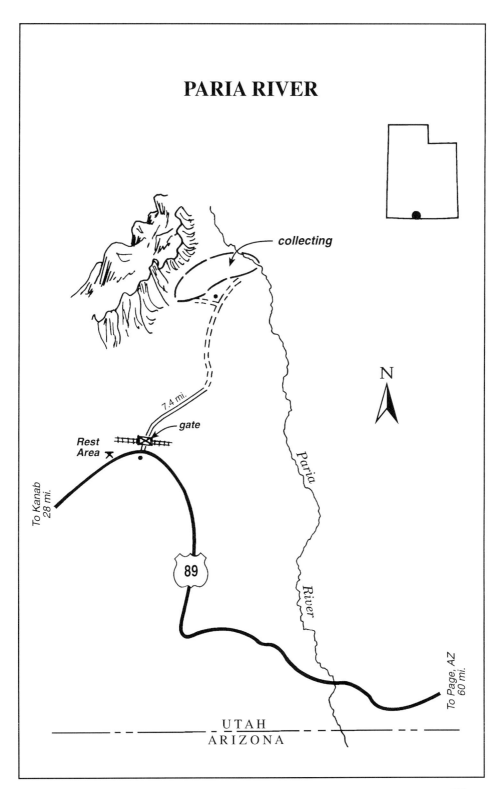

collecting

N

7.4 mi.

gate

Rest
Area

To Kanab
28 mi.

89

Paria

River

To Page, AZ
60 mi.

UTAH
ARIZONA

The hills west of Orderville are the source of one of Utah's best known mineralogical exports, the septarium nodule. The word "septarium" means a roughly spherical concretion with a compact crust and an internal mass broken with angular cracks that widen toward the center and are filled, or partly filled, with a foreign mineral or crystals. That is a perfect description of the nodules found here.

Because of their value, much of the area is protected by private claims, but rockhounds are often allowed onto those claims if permission is procured beforehand. It should be noted that these fascinating mineralogical oddities are generally found many feet below the surface and tractors are required to get down deep enough. The only thing that hobby collectors will find are fragments or specimens that have been exposed by erosion, primarily near Muddy Creek, or ones that are intentionally (or accidentally) left behind by the claimholders.

One of the claims is governed by Tetla Septariums, a rock shop in Orderville. Access, however, tends to be sporadic, and a fee might be required. Up-to-date information is available at the shop. The claims most consistently open to rockhounds are owned by Joe's Rock Shop, on Highway 89, just south of town. The place is shaped like a big rock and is on the east side of the road. At time of publication, there is no charge to enter those claims, but permission must be granted before heading in. Since the roads

traverse slick clay, travel is impossible, even with four-wheel drive, when the ground is wet. Therefore, a call to Joe's Rock Shop before your visit might save some frustration. The number is (801) 648-2425.

Nodules, most of which are broken, can be procured on either of the claims, in spite of the fact that commercial mining is taking place. Collecting is done on both sides of Muddy Creek, covering an extensive area. Some regions are tough to get to, however, without four-wheel drive. More information can be obtained when you secure collecting permission.

Digging for nodules

74

MT. CARMEL

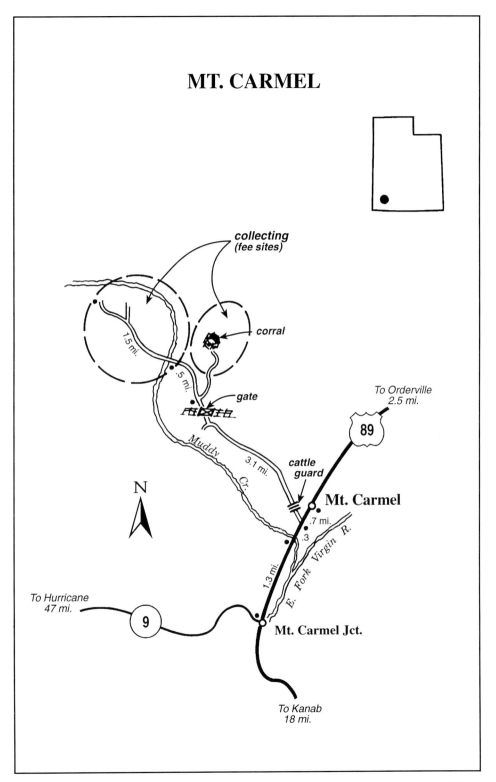

collecting
(fee sites)

corral

1.5 mi.

.5 mi.

gate

To Orderville
2.5 mi.

89

Muddy Cr.

3.1 mi.

cattle
guard

N

Mt. Carmel

.7 mi.

.3

E. Fork Virgin R.

1.3 mi.

To Hurricane
47 mi.

9

Mt. Carmel Jct.

To Kanab
18 mi.

This site offers collectors fine samples of pyrite cubes, feldspar, quartz, biotite, hornblende, limonite, and colorful rhyolite. It is situated within a hydrothermal contact zone in the Wah Wah Mountains, about thirty-one miles west of Milford. The zone of mineralization is exposed in a very accessible road cut on Highway 21, and there is plenty of room to safely pull off the pavement. The rhyolite is confined within the intrusive igneous body, while the other minerals are found primarily within the contact region.

To get to the center of this mineralogically rich area, go west thirty-one miles from Milford, on Highway 21, to milepost 46. From there, continue one-half mile more to the primary mineral-bearing road cut on the right. Probably the best place to collect is within the large road cut itself, but additional specimens can be gathered throughout the terrain above. Basically, good collecting potential is afforded just about anywhere the native limestone has been intruded by the igneous rhyolite.

Carefully break away suspect portions of the metamorphized areas and inspect them for mineral/crystal content. If you find nothing worthwhile, just continue the procedure at another spot until you do find something. If you locate a particularly good location, you may want to employ a pry bar and other heavier tools to attempt removing larger chunks of the mineral-bearing, host rock.

Parked off the pavement

WAH WAH MOUNTAINS

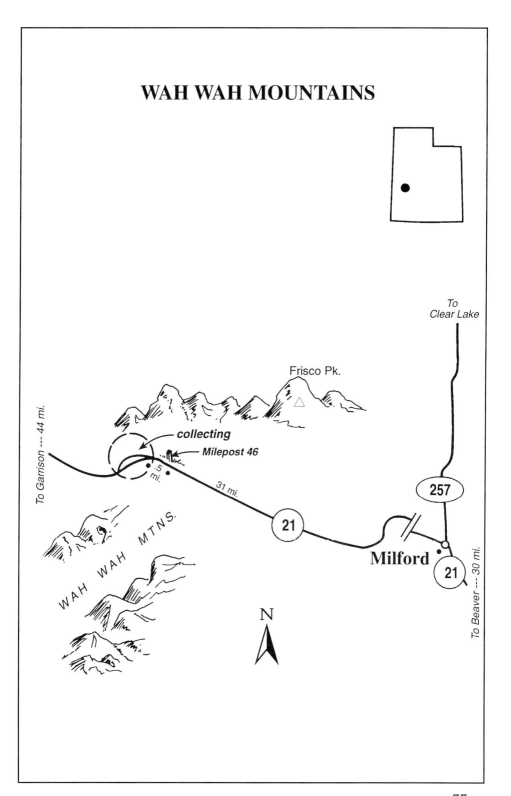

Frisco Pk.

To Garrison --- 44 mi.

collecting

Milepost 46

.5 mi.

31 mi.

WAH WAH MTNS.

21

To Clear Lake

257

Milford

21

To Beaver --- 30 mi.

N

Very little is left of the once booming town of Old Frisco, nestled in the eastern foothills of San Francisco Mountain. At one time, more than 4,000 people lived in the prosperous silver town, but, by 1920, nobody was left. The main shaft had collapsed and it was determined to be uneconomical to reopen the mine. Today, however, the abandoned mine dumps at Old Frisco and those on the western side of the mountain offer collectors the opportunity to find a wide variety of mineral specimens including pyrite, galena, sphalerite, selenite, Apache tears, and chalcopyrite.

To get there, drive fifteen miles west from Milford on Highway 21. At that point, there is a historical plaque on the north side of the highway commemorating Old Frisco. The road leading to what remains of the town is situated next to the historical marker.

The best way to get good specimens is to dig in the dumps with pick and shovel. Use a hammer and chisel to split all suspect rocks in order to determine if they contain anything worthwhile. When exploring the town, it is not advisable to enter the old buildings, since they are all very unstable. Also, be certain not to venture into any mine shafts. It has also been reported over the years that a few people have been living in Old Frisco. If that is the case when you visit, be certain to respect their rights.

There is another road three and seven-tenths miles farther west, along Highway 21, which leads north to additional dumps. They are a little tougher to get to than those at Old Frisco and, therefore, fewer people have collected there, affording the potential for finding better and larger specimens. If you have time and a rugged vehicle, be sure to explore that area also.

Abandoned buildings at Old Frisco

OLD FRISCO

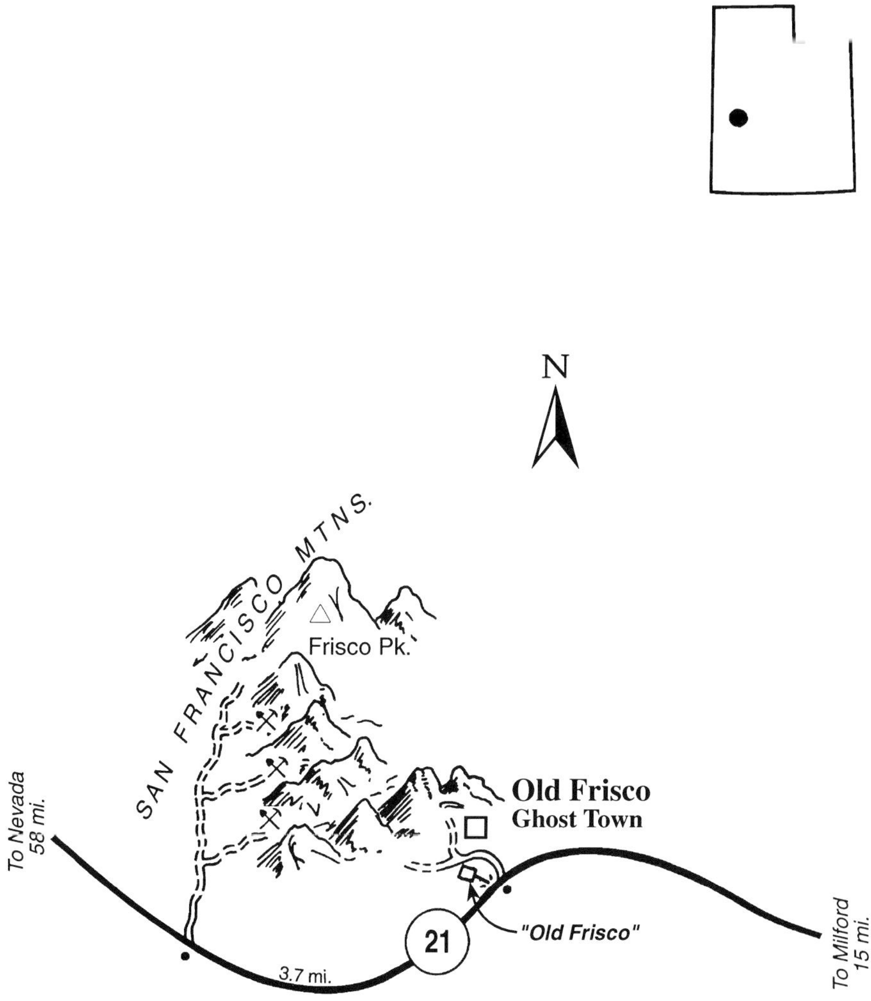

N

SAN FRANCISCO MTNS.

△ Frisco Pk.

Old Frisco
Ghost Town

To Nevada
58 mi.

21

"Old Frisco"

3.7 mi.

To Milford
15 mi.

This old mining area is so extensive that plenty of time should be set aside in order to thoroughly explore it. To get to the center of the region with best collecting potential, go west from Milford, on Highway 21, for one mile and then turn north another four and seven-tenths miles, as shown on the map. At that point, dumps will be seen in the surrounding hills, for quite a distance. All afford good potential, just be certain to only gather minerals on prospects where rockhounding is permitted.

Of primary interest is the colorful chrysocolla, malachite, azurite, and bornite. Collecting here is easy, because those brightly colored minerals stand out vividly against the gray dumps. If you want more than surface material, it is often productive to do some light digging in order to expose specimens that would otherwise be hidden. Be very careful if you do decide to dig, since the dumps are very rocky and not too stable, making it easy to slip.

Primarily, the copper ores are only thin surface deposits, but some is thick enough to polish, even though most must be left attached to a portion of the host rock for extra support and stability.

The biggest collecting problem here is to decide what to take and what to leave behind. Since specimens are so colorful, that decision is often painful. It takes time to carefully examine each piece in order to pick out only the best.

As is the case with any old mine, the collecting status is always subject to change. Be certain that the dumps are still abandoned when you visit, BEFORE you collect.

Exploring the old mine dumps

WEST OF MILFORD

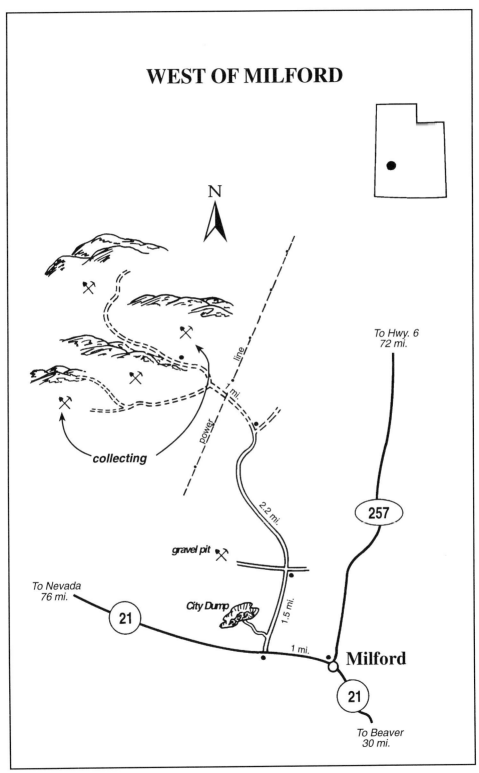

To Hwy. 6
72 mi.

257

collecting

power line

1 mi.

2.2 mi.

gravel pit

To Nevada
76 mi.

21

City Dump

1.5 mi.

1 mi.

Milford

21

To Beaver
30 mi.

Both of these sites offer the collector lots of black, mahogany, and snow-flake obsidian, much of which is very good quality. Since the routes to both require crossing washes and loose sand, four-wheel drive is highly recommended, even though most rugged vehicles should have little trouble.

To get to Site A, go south on Highway 257 approximately thirty-seven miles from where it intersects Highway 6/50. At that point, there is a dirt road heading east and a forest sign designating it as the route to Kanosh. Follow that road two and two-tenths miles to where ruts intersect from the south. Follow them through the wash three-tenths of a mile to a sandy quarry, which is the center of Site A. From there, for quite a distance in all directions, one can find tons of obsidian in sizes ranging from pebbles and chips to boulders.

Site B is reached by returning to the highway and proceeding ten and six-tenths miles farther south to a sign giving mileage to Antelope Spring and Highway 91. Go east on the dirt road two and two-tenths miles. Proceed right onto ruts to a gate in the range fence, being certain to reclose it after passing through. From there, follow the dim tracks about three-tenths of a mile as they double back toward the ridge overlooking the valley and highway.

At Site B collectors can find much of the same material as at Site A but it seems to be more scarce and much smaller. Be sure to walk a distance from wherever you park, since the obsidian is not evenly distributed. Some areas are covered with material and, at other spots, nothing can be found.

Searching for material at Site A

BLACK ROCK

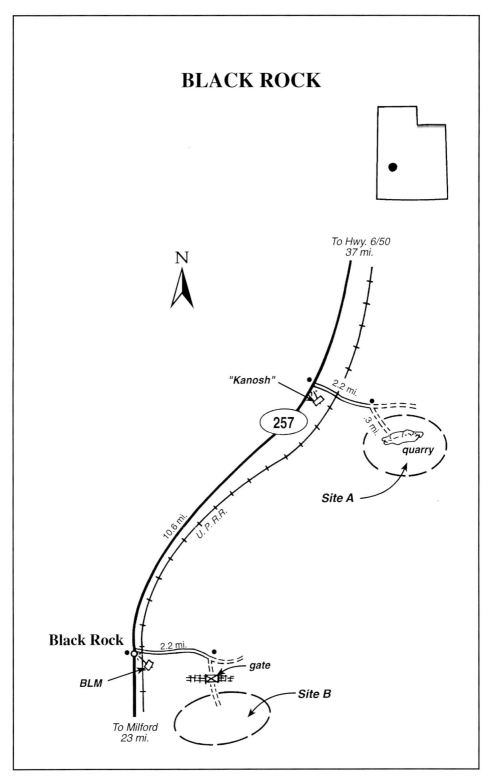

N

To Hwy. 6/50
37 mi.

"Kanosh"

257

2.2 mi.

.3 mi.

quarry

Site A

10.6 mi.

U.P. R.R.

Black Rock

2.2 mi.

gate

BLM

Site B

To Milford
23 mi.

These two sites, both near the town of Milford, offer collectors fine mineral specimens and tons of cutting quality obsidian. To reach Site A, go north from town on Highway 257, four and one-half miles, and turn right onto County Road 1034, toward the Blundell Geothermal Plant. The road is paved for the first one and two-tenths miles and then well graded beyond there. Go a total of nine and eight-tenths miles, passing the geothermal power plant, and park.

At that point, the ground is covered with good quality obsidian, most of which is black, but lots of mahogany and snowflake material can also be found. Additional obsidian can be obtained for quite a distance in any direction, and it might be productive to drive or hike a little farther to see what can be found.

To reach Site B, which is actually a series of mine dumps, return to Milford and head south eleven and four-tenths miles on Highway 21. At that point, you will see a very rough road heading northeast toward the mountains. This road is passable by most rugged vehicles, and unless there has been recent heavy rain, four-wheel drive is probably not needed. The first of the dumps is about three and one-half miles from the highway. On that dump, and those farther up the road, one can pick up fine specimens of fluorite, pyrite, magnetite, bornite, galena, quartz, and a host of other minerals.

Don't forget that the ownership and collecting status of old mines can frequently change. Be certain that any dump you visit is abandoned, or secure permission to collect there beforehand.

View of Site A

MILFORD AREA

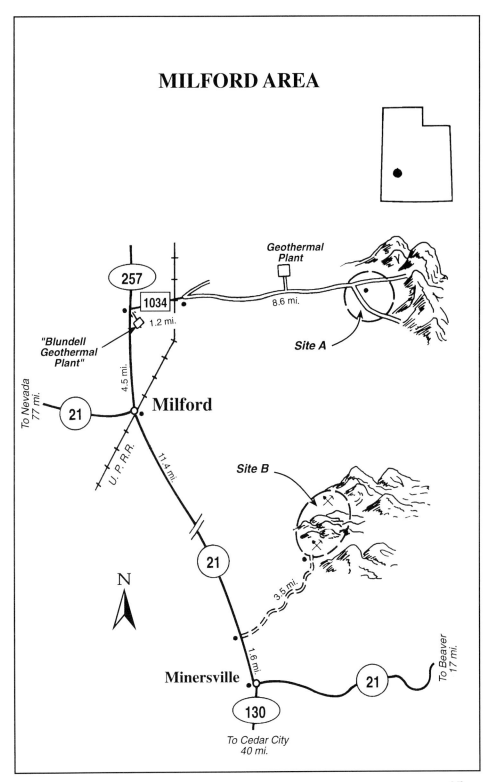

257

1034

Geothermal Plant

8.6 mi.

Site A

"Blundell Geothermal Plant"

1.2 mi.

4.5 mi.

To Nevada 77 mi.

21

Milford

U. P. R. R.

11.4 mi.

Site B

21

N

3.5 mi.

1.6 mi.

Minersville

21

To Beaver 17 mi.

130

To Cedar City 40 mi.

Colorful pieces of common opal can be gathered a short distance north of Milford. Some of the material is banded, in contrasting colors, while other pieces can be found exhibiting an interesting bubbly surface texture. Colors range from violet, red, and maroon to white and blue.

This location has traditionally been a privately held claim, most recently governed by the Utah Federation of Gem and Mineralogical Societies, and a small fee was charged to collect there. There is usually some sort of sign posted near the diggings explaining payment procedures, but, at time of publication, no such sign was there. Be certain to make every effort to pay, if still required, since the Federation is leasing the land in order to keep it open to collectors, and the money is used to help defray the lease and maintenance costs.

To get there, go north from Milford on Highway 257, four and one-half miles, and turn right onto County Road 1034, toward the Geothermal Plant. The road is paved for the first one and two-tenths miles and then well graded most of the way from there. Drive a total of seven and three-tenths miles from the highway and a rutted road will be encountered on the right, as illustrated on the map. Follow those tracks two-tenths of a mile to the ridge and then turn right another three-tenths of a mile to the digging pits.

The opal seams are easy to spot, looking almost plastic-like in and around the excavations. Working the seams, however, is difficult work and extreme care must be taken not to fracture the somewhat delicate material. If you don't feel like engaging in the tough digging and hard rock work, there is lots of opal scattered on the surface throughout the surrounding terrain. Most, however, is fractured or somewhat colorless, but occasional colorful specimens can be found.

Searching for common opal

NORTH OF MILFORD

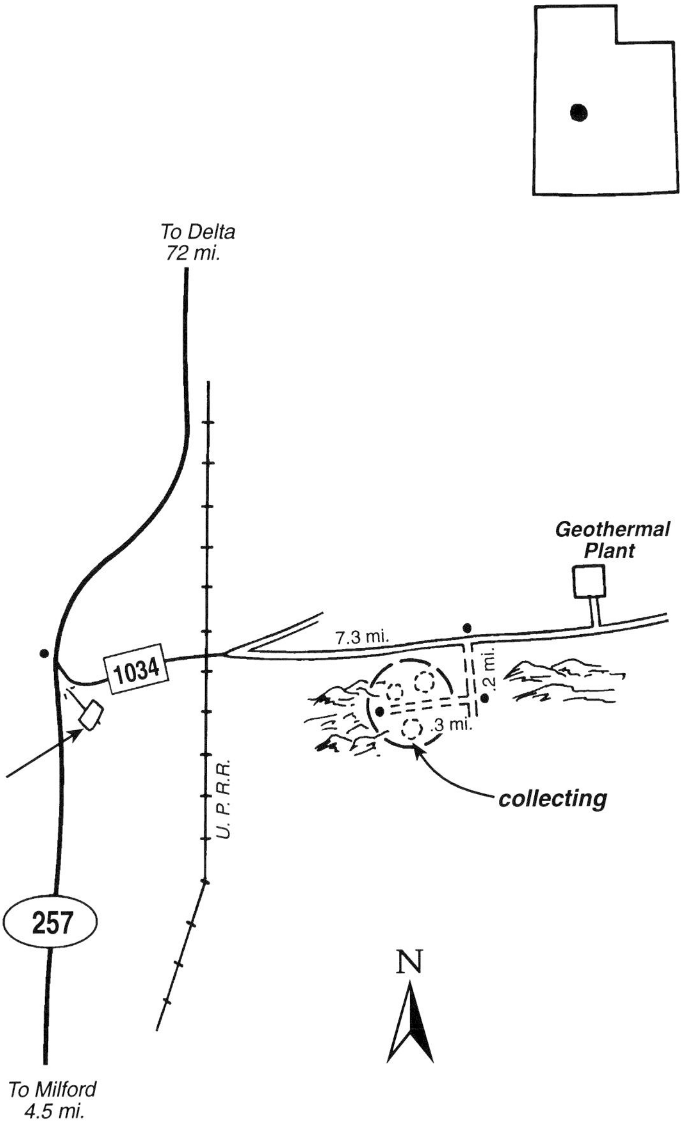

To Delta
72 mi.

Geothermal
Plant

7.3 mi.

1034

.2 mi.

"Blundell
Geothermal
Plant"

.3 mi.

U. P. R.R.

collecting

257

N

To Milford
4.5 mi.

For decades, this has been a consistently productive location for rockhounds to gather wonderstone. In spite of such heavy use, collectors are still able to find top quality, fine-grained material, much of which will take a dull polish. The colors range from light tan to dark brown, with some displaying maroon and red bands. To make things even better, the patterns are frequently symmetrical, thereby being very suitable for cabochons, bolo ties, brooches, and belt buckles. Material taken from the wider seams can frequently be used for bookends, spheres, and other more sizable items. Take a sledge hammer, some chisels and gads, as well as a heavy pry bar.

Over the years, at some of the easier to get to spots, people have tunneled into the side of the mountain, leaving potentially dangerous overhangs. Be sure to break down any such hazardous areas before starting work. A hard-hat is also recommended in such situations.

Collectors can occasionally find fossil fish and other marine life embedded within the native shale. Carefully split it along bedding planes and examine the freshly exposed surfaces for traces of the elusive fossils.

To get to this locality, start at the four-way stop in Salina, where Highway 50 intersects Highway 89. From there, as shown on the map, proceed on Main Street, as if Highway 50 went straight ahead, for three-tenths of a mile, and then turn right onto 300 E Street. Go three and seven-tenths miles, passing City Park, and then paralleling the northern side of Interstate 70.

At the given mileage, turn right, pass under the interstate, and, on the opposite side, follow Paiute Trail 01 two and seven-tenths miles to a large BLM sign providing mileage to Mud Springs and a number of other locations. Proceed right onto Forest Road 048, go three-tenths of a mile farther, bear left onto the ruts, and park. Signs of digging along the wonderstone seams can be seen on just about all of the surrounding hills, with the most accessible portion being just ahead, to the right of where you park.

Removing the wonderstone from the seam

SALINA CANYON

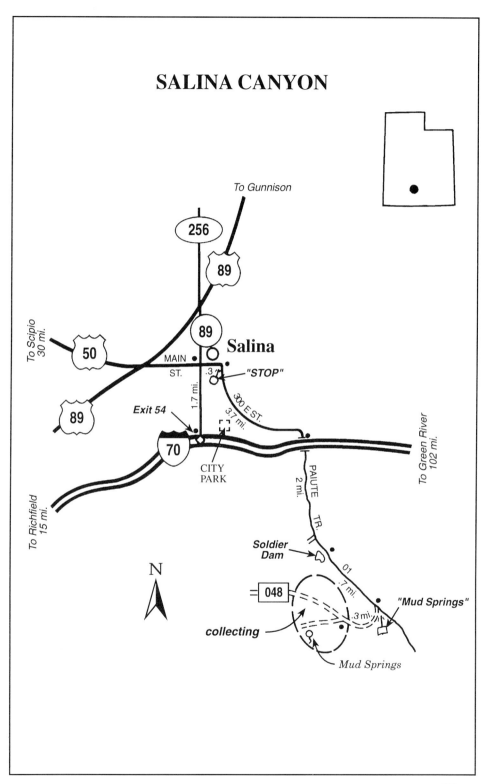

To Gunnison

256

89

89

Salina

To Scipio
30 mi.

50

MAIN ST.

.3

"STOP"

89

Exit 54

1.7 mi.

300 E ST.

3.7 mi.

70

CITY PARK

To Green River
102 mi.

To Richfield
15 mi.

PAIUTE TR.
2 mi.

N

Soldier Dam

01

.7 mi.

048

"Mud Springs"

.3 mi.

collecting

Mud Springs

This site is situated near some of the most spectacular scenery in the entire United States. Even if you weren't a mineral collector, a visit to this region would be a memorable one.

To get to the collecting area, which boasts beautiful red and white agate, drive six-tenths of a mile east from the Capitol Reef National Park eastern boundary to the well-graded, dirt road heading south. There is a sign on the highway designating this as the road to Notom. Proceed three and one-half miles to a major intersection from which you should bear straight ahead another two and nine-tenths miles. At that point, turn left, and drive four-tenths of a mile on the road going into the hills. This is the beginning of the collecting site.

The agate is primarily found in the greenish clay of the Curtis Formation which can be seen northeast of the road, but lots of very nice material is also scattered about in all directions throughout the flatlands for quite a distance. You will probably be very satisfied with what can be obtained from the surface, but if you want to try your luck at digging in the Curtis clay, you may find additional material. Don't hesitate to look near the cliffs to the north.

Much of the agate is white, but lots of it contains areas of vivid red. Since pieces with both colors can be used to produce very nice polished pieces, a special effort should be made to find some.

Parked at the collecting site

NOTOM

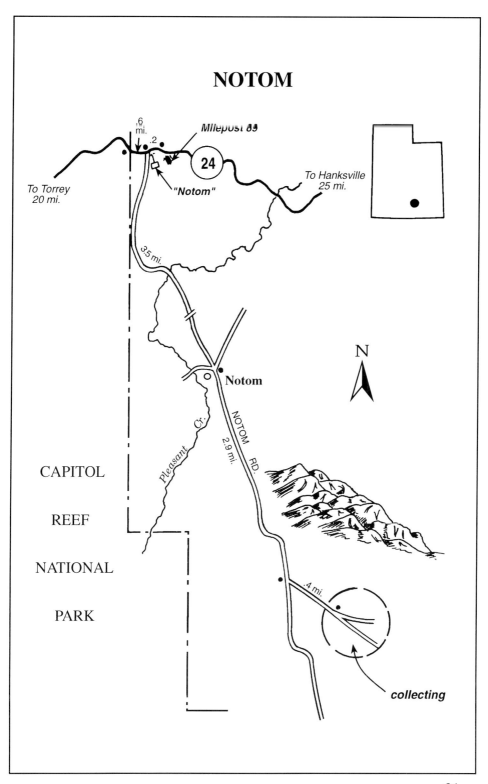

Milepost 89

(24)

.6 mi.

.2

"Notom"

To Torrey
20 mi.

To Hanksville
25 mi.

3.5 mi.

N

○ Notom

Pleasant Cr.

NOTOM RD.

2.9 mi.

CAPITOL

REEF

NATIONAL

PARK

.4 mi.

collecting

Caineville is situated about twenty miles west of Hanksville, on Highway 24. This collecting site is actually six miles east of town, between milepost 105 and milepost 106, on either side of the road. Just park in a safe place, well off the pavement, and plan to do some walking.

The list of what can be found scattered about the surrounding terrain includes colorful agate, chert, selenite, and jasper, as well as petrified wood. The agate, jasper and chert are relatively easy to find, since their colors contrast with that of the soil, even though nothing is especially large. In fact, the agate and some of the chert looks almost white against the darker soil. The jasper is a little more subtle in contrast, but its nice gold, yellow and occasional red does make spotting relatively easy. Look for the selenite "growing" in the soft soil of the conspicuous hills throughout the collecting area.

The wood is much darker and thereby tougher to see. It is nice, though, and well worth looking for. Some of the specimens have retained much of the wood's original structure and actually look just like little twigs and pieces of limbs. Lots of the wood, however, is porous and/or pitted and it takes some effort to find chunks capable of taking a good polish. The porous material is often nice, unpolished, for display in a mineral collection.

The concentration seems random, and if you don't find much at one spot, either keep hiking or drive a little farther and repeat the procedure. If you have a rugged vehicle, there are some tracks leading off the highway to potentially more prolific deposits. Since much of the more easily gathered material near the paved highway has already been taken, following such roads for even a short distance could very well prove to be worthwhile.

Tracks that lead off the highway to additional deposits

CAINEVILLE

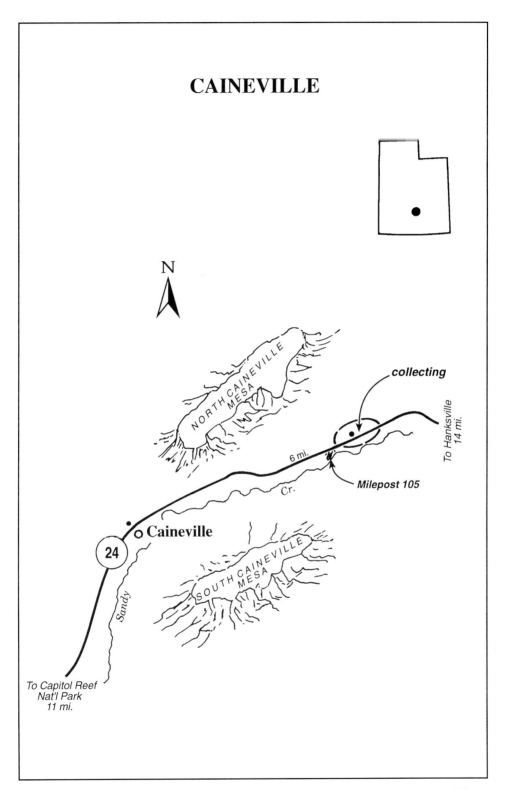

N

collecting

To Hanksville
14 mi.

NORTH CAINEVILLE MESA

6 mi.

Cr.

Milepost 105

SOUTH CAINEVILLE MESA

• ○ **Caineville**

24

Sandy

To Capitol Reef
Nat'l Park
11 mi.

The region northwest of prominent Factory Butte offers rockhounds very nice and often colorful agate. To get to this somewhat extensive agate field, simply start at milepost 98, go east one-half mile, and turn north onto Caineville Wash Road. Bear right at the first fork, located about two-tenths of a mile from the highway, continue north until you have gone two and one-half miles from the pavement, and then turn right.

From that point, the going gets rough. You will encounter lots of loose sand and there may be periodic washouts which must be circumnavigated. For that reason, this trip is only suggested to those with rugged four-wheel drive units. It is also advisable to have another such vehicle with you on the journey, just in case one gets stuck.

Continue another seven rough miles and, just before reaching the old mine, turn left and continue about four-tenths of a mile to the southeast edge of the collecting site. That last stretch may or may not be driveable and it might be necessary to park at the mine and hike the rest of the way.

The agate is scattered randomly for quite a distance north and west and features some extremely desirable red and yellow material, some of which also contains interesting black inclusions. It is associated with the greenish clay of the Curtis Formation. Some digging with pick and shovel into that somewhat soft material might produce additional specimens.

Road to Factory Butte

FACTORY BUTTE

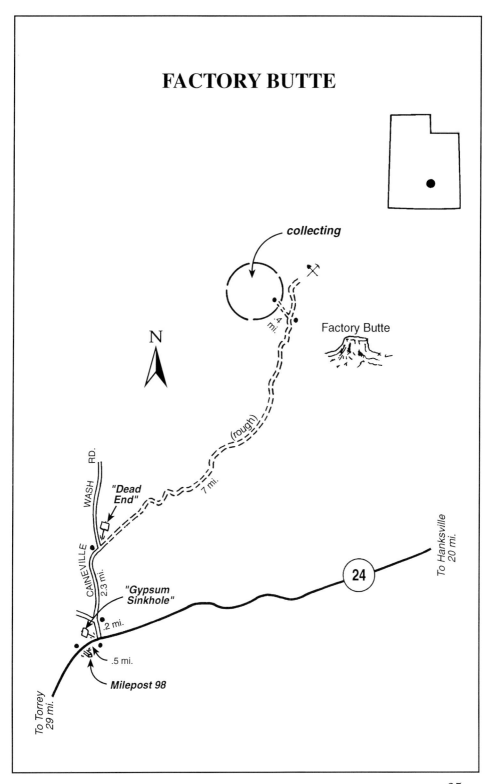

collecting

Factory Butte

N

(rough)

.4 mi.

7 mi.

WASH RD.

"Dead End"

CAINEVILLE

2.3 mi.

"Gypsum Sinkhole"

.2 mi.

24

To Hanksville 20 mi.

.5 mi.

Milepost 98

To Torrey 29 mi.

UTAH'S OTHER ATTRACTIONS

Between rockhounding trips enjoy some of Utah's other attractions. From the urban sophistication of Salt Lake City in the north, to the stunning beauty of five national parks in the south, there is something for everyone. The state of Utah is renown for its spectacular scenery, unlimited recreational opportunities, fascinating geology, picturesque countryside, and rugged mountains, not to mention its bountiful mineralogical resources. When many people think of Utah, visions of deserts and stark, barren cliffs come to mind. Granted, the state does boast such areas, but it is also a vacationer's paradise. The cool pines and refreshing streams and rivers, within the central mountainous band which stretches virtually the entire length of the state, have drawn vacationers for decades.

Recreational opportunites are available throughout the state for all ages and all interests. There are countless lakes, including the colossal Great Salt Lake and Utah Lake, for swimming, boating and water skiing. River running and rafting is popular on numerous rivers. Hikers can enjoy incredibly spectacular scenery featuring the beautifully sculpted and colorful geological formations of Bryce Canyon National Park, Arches National Park, Capitol Reef National Park, Canyonlands National Park, Cedar Breaks National Monument, Natural Bridges National Monument, Rainbow Bridge National Monument, and Zion National Park. Furthermore, Utah boasts six national forests, forty-eight state parks and over 22 million acres of land managed by the BLM.

Some of the beautiful scenery at Capitol Reef National Park

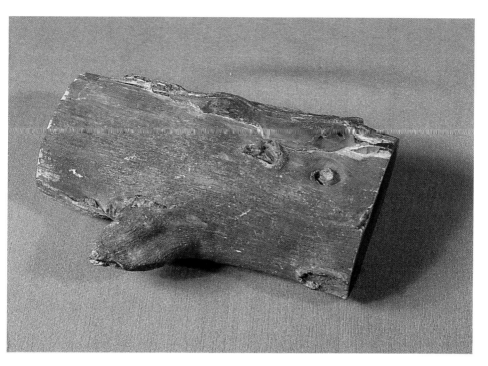

Petrified wood found at the Paria River collecting site

Malachite and calcite on limonite from Gold Hill

Petrified wood from Escalante

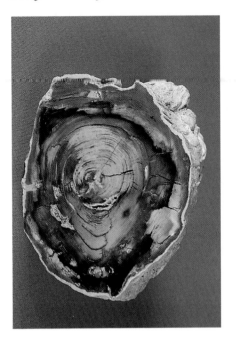

Red horn coral fossil found at the Woodland site

Wonderstone gathered at the Salina Canyon collecting area

Sand selenite discovered at the San Rafael site

Fossil collected in northern Utah

Selenite found at Caineville

Obsidian from the Black Rock area

Barite balls discovered at Cisco and Yellow Cat

Feldspar and mica specimen

Galena sample collected at Silver City

Moss opalite — Eureka

Bornite found near Milford

Sphalerite, hematite and quartz

Iron concretions from Spencer Flat

Common opal collected north of Milford

Petrified wood — Little Creek Mountain

Malachite and azurite — Silver City   *An especially fine sample of malachite*

Calcite and galena found in the Milford area at Site B

Septarium nodule from Mt. Carmel

Feldspar and sphalerite collected at Old Frisco

Skiing is very popular in Utah. Coss-country and alpine ski conditions rank among the top in the world. Utah license plates claim Utah has the "Greatest Snow On Earth." When the weather warms up, Utah's reputation as a bicycling destination is well earned on both alpine and red rock trails. For skiing information and other statewide attractions contact the Utah Travel Council, Council Hall/Capitol Hill, Salt Lake City, UT 84114-1396, (801) 538-1030 or toll free at (800) 200-1160.

Located in the heart of the American West, sites of historic significance abound in Utah. Learn about the ancient Anasazi people at Newspaper Rock near Moab, the Parowan Gap Petroglyphs near Cedar City and Hovenweep National Monument in southeastern Utah. Get a glimpse of Utah's pioneer days by traveling along the Pony Express Trail, or by visiting the Golden Spike National Historic Site outside of Brigham City, the Camp Floyd Stagecoach Inn State Park northwest of Provo, or the Donner-Reed Pioneer Museum in Grantsville.

Countless additional regions of geological and recreational significance include Dinosaur National Monument on the Colorado/Utah border, Flaming Gorge National Recreation Area in northeastern Utah, the Tintic Mining Museum in Eureka, the Utah Museum of Natural History in Salt Lake City, the Cleveland-Lloyd Dinosaur Quarry south of Price, Glen Canyon National Recreation Area on the Utah/Arizona border, and Timpanogos Cave National Monument north of Provo.

Cultural entertainment abounds in Salt Lake, along with historical sights, shopping, dining, and other big city amenities. For specific attractions, contact the Salt Lake Convention & Visitors Bureau, 180 S. West Temple, Salt Lake City, UT 84101, (801) 521-2822.

Colorful jasper, agate and interesting, fossilized, oyster shells can all be gathered from a deposit situated only a short distance from where Highway 24 crosses the Fremont River. If you are interested, go six-tenths of a mile northeast from the bridge, as illustrated on the map, and park in a safe spot, well off the pavement. The collecting area is centered in and around the purplish little hills, accessed by following the very faint remnants of what used to be a road, as it heads northward for about 100 yards.

Chunks of the shell-bearing rock, as well as the colorful agate and jasper, are easily spotted. It is possible to obtain specimens directly from their place in the hill, but most collectors are very satisfied with what can be found already removed by the forces of nature. Just walk throughout the region and examine any suspicious rock for embedded ancient oysters or signs of color associated with the agate and jasper. Some chunks are far better for display than others, so be sure to allow plenty of time to find the very best pieces.

If you are not satisfied with the quality of fossils found scattered on the ground, portions of the deposit can be removed directly from the hill, but such a project takes time. First of all, care must be taken not to damage the delicate shells, so the resulting pieces provide the best possible specimens for collections. It definitely takes considerable patience and even a certain amount of luck to remove portions of a size and quality worthy of display. Look for places of weakness, such as already existing fractures along the fossil-bearing rock, as a place to start.

Gathering agate, jasper and fossilized oyster shells

FREMONT RIVER

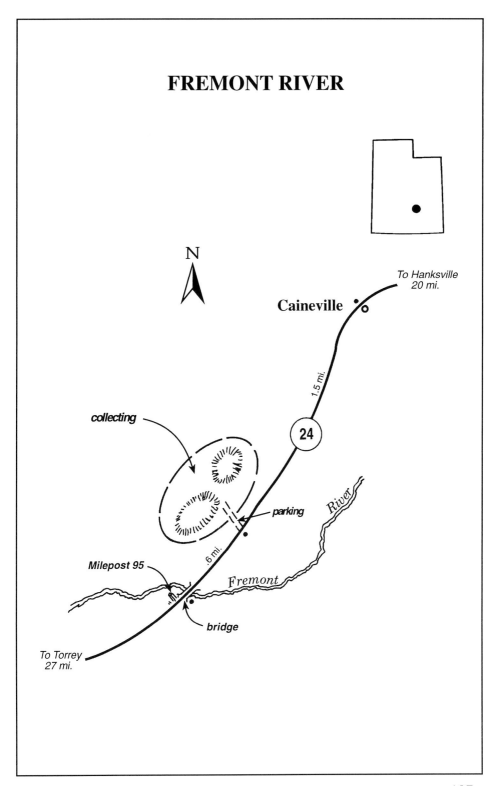

N

To Hanksville
20 mi.

Caineville

1.5 mi.

24

collecting

parking

River

.6 mi.

Milepost 95

Fremont

bridge

To Torrey
27 mi.

This extensive collecting area, situated a short distance west of Hanksville, offers rockhounds an opportunity to obtain lots of colorful agate, jasper, and petrified wood.

In addition to the good collecting opportunities, the site is surrounded by seven incredibly scenic areas. To the west is Zion National Park, Cedar Breaks National Monument, Capitol Reef National Park, and Bryce Canyon National Park; to the east is Canyonlands National Park and Arches National Park; while to the south is Glen Canyon National Recreation Area. Obviously, rockhounds aren't the only people interested in this part of the country.

The collecting site is reached by taking Highway 24 west from Hanksville eleven miles. At that point, on the right, you will see a stop sign and a paved road leading north. Heading south from the highway are some ruts. In addition, there is a large butte to the northwest, which makes a good landmark. Go south on the ruts only a few tenths of a mile into the shallow hills and park. This is a good spot from which to start your collecting.

Agate and jasper can be found scattered all over, but the wood is a little more difficult to find. The material tends to be small, but what it lacks in size is made up for in color and quality. Don't hesitate to do some walking, since this field seems to extend for quite a distance. Pay particularly close attention to areas of erosion for larger chunks. You should be able to pick up quite a bit in a short amount of time, especially if you hike a bit.

WEST OF HANKSVILLE

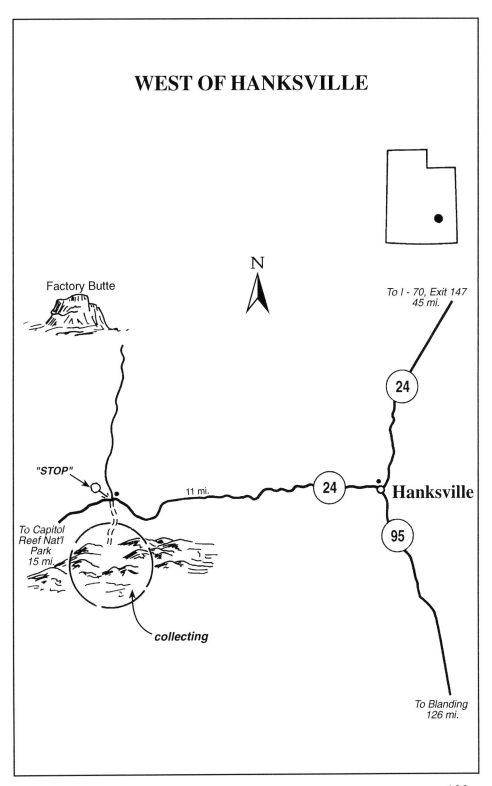

Factory Butte

N

To I - 70, Exit 147
45 mi.

24

"STOP"

11 mi.

24

Hanksville

To Capitol
Reef Nat'l
Park
15 mi.

95

collecting

To Blanding
126 mi.

These four sites offer collectors an opportunity to find agate, jasper, petrified wood, picture-stone, and even some dinosaur bone. To get to Site A, head south from Hanksville on Highway 95 to Highway 276. Continue on Highway 276 sixteen and seven-tenths miles, then turn right toward Star Springs. This road is rough in places, but most rugged vehicles should have no trouble if the ground is dry. Drive past Star Springs and Shootering Canyon to Hansen Creek, about ten and one-tenth miles from the highway. Turn left onto the ruts which are encountered immediately after crossing the creek, and proceed one more mile to the colorful mounds on the left.

This is the northern edge of Site A. From there, continuing into the canyon at least two more miles, one can find lots of colorful red agate, bubbly grape agate, an occasional piece of jasper, petrified wood, and dinosaur bone. Pay particularly close attention to the mounds and adjacent terrain.

To reach Site B, return to the main road and travel three and seven-tenths more miles. At that point, you will be next to a small canyon, and lots of agate and jasper chips can be found on the flatlands above it. Down below, you should be able to get larger chunks. This is called the "chipping ground" and is thought to be where, long ago, Indians came to make arrowheads from the plentiful agate supply. Most of the agate is red although other colors can also be found.

From Site B, go one and seven-tenths miles on the main road, turn left another four and one-tenth miles, and then left a few tenths of a mile on the very rough and steep set of ruts to Site C. The last stretch probably requires four-wheel drive or, at the very least, a rugged vehicle. Site C boasts lots of

nice red agate, as well as some purple and white material. In addition, a few tenths of a mile to the north, is an outcrop of picture-stone rhyolite.

Site D is accessed from Hanksville by going three miles west on Highway 24 and then taking the dirt road north about five and one-half miles to Muddy Creek. Walk along the creek to find more agate.

Site B

HANKSVILLE

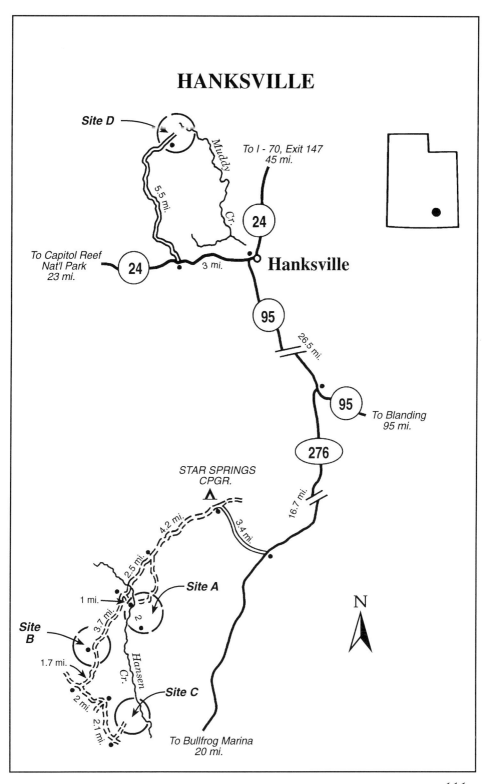

Site D

Muddy Cr.

To I - 70, Exit 147
45 mi.

5.5 mi.

24

To Capitol Reef
Nat'l Park
23 mi.

24

3 mi.

Hanksville

95

26.5 mi.

95

To Blanding
95 mi.

276

*STAR SPRINGS
CPGR.*

16.7 mi.

4.2 mi.

3.4 mi.

2.5 mi.

Site A

1 mi.

3.7 mi.

2

Site
B

1.7 mi.

Hansen
Cr.

Site C

2 mi.

2.1 mi.

To Bullfrog Marina
20 mi.

N

Good specimens of colorful petrified wood can be found deep within scenic Horse Canyon, located about twenty-three miles southeast of Boulder. To get to this favored location, take the Burr Trail out of Boulder, as shown on the map. It is a fair dirt road and rugged vehicles should have little trouble unless there have been recent heavy rains.

After going six and one-half miles, you will cross Deer Creek. Another four miles places you at The Gulch, a popular recreation site. Continue approximately six and one-half more miles to where there is a BLM sign and an intersecting road. It is there where you should turn right and continue another four and one-half miles to where ruts can be seen heading off to the right into Horse Canyon wash. There are some trees on the west at this intersection, helping to make the turnoff easier to spot.

Follow the ruts approximately one-half mile into the canyon. From that point, due to loose sand, you should park and walk, unless you have four-wheel drive. Proceed another one-half mile to the base of the cliffs which marks the start of the collecting area. You should be able to find some small pieces of wood randomly lying about. If you want sizable specimens, it will probably be necessary to do some heavy digging into the red and blue Chinle Formation which can be seen throughout the area.

If you have the time, the main road is known as the Petrified Forest Loop, and it takes you on a thirty mile journey through lots of additional wood-bearing areas. If you have a sense of adventure, you might want to try a few of the side roads along that route, just to see if they might lead to something worthwhile. Even if you don't find much of anything, it is a very pleasant, but rough, drive.

Searching for petrified wood

HORSE CANYON

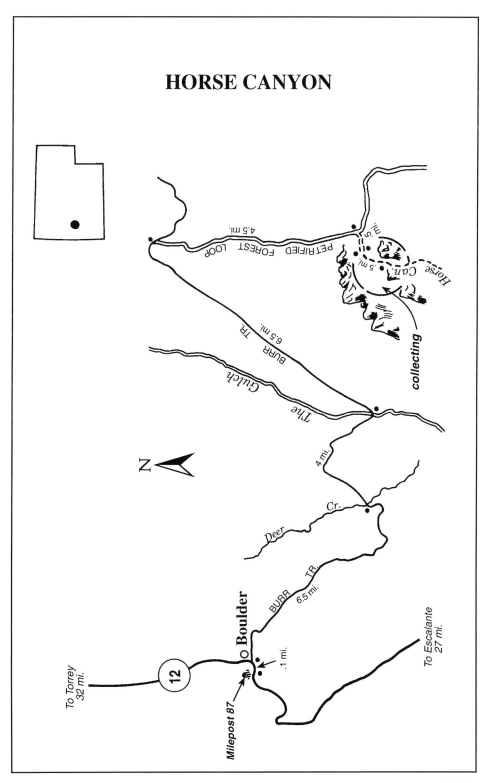

These two sites offer rockhounds fascinating spherical iron concretions (Site A) and colorful jasper and agate (Site B).

To get to Site A, which is one of Utah's most unusual collecting areas, follow Highway 12 about ten miles east from Escalante to where a difficult-to-spot dirt road intersects from the right. If you are coming from the east, you will probably have to pass the road and then double back. Turn, and proceed five miles from the highway to the beginning of the site.

From there, and continuing at least another two miles, on either side of the road, lots of black and brown, spherical, iron concretions can be found. You will find lots of broken spheres and very small, marble-sized specimens near the road. The larger specimens require some walking into less accessible locations.

There is a legend that when the Moqui Indians lived in the area they used the smaller balls to play games like marbles and the larger ones for throwing and catching. The most prolific collecting seems to be near the conspicuous hill about a half mile from the road.

Site B is reached by returning to Highway 12 and heading thirteen and three-tenths miles toward Boulder. At that point, which is just before Hell's Backbone Road turnoff, you can pick up jasper and agate, primarily in shades of red and yellow, on both sides of the road. Most is small, but some larger chunks, usually partially buried, can be found. Agate chips and flakes litter the terrain throughout Site B, supporting the theory that this was one of the places where the Moqui Indians came for material to make their arrows, knives, and other tools.

Hiking toward the hill at Site A

SPENCER FLAT

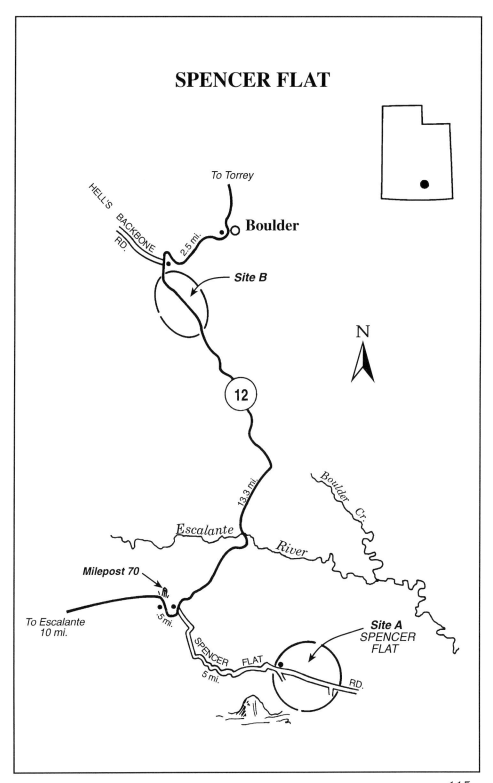

To Torrey

HELL'S BACKBONE RD.

2.5 mi.

○ **Boulder**

Site B

N

12

Boulder Cr.

Escalante

River

13.3 mi.

Milepost 70

.5 mi.

To Escalante
10 mi.

SPENCER FLAT

5 mi.

RD.

Site A
SPENCER
FLAT

To get to the first of these three collecting sites, go north from the school building, in Escalante, approximately two miles. At the given mileage, you will be at a cattle guard, which is the landmark for Site A. Jasper, agate, calcite and onyx can be picked up primarily on the right side of the road but it is scarce. Some hiking away from the easily accessible areas will be required if you want to find much. Patient exploration is necessary to find worthwhile quantities, but the extra time and effort is often rewarded.

Site B is reached by continuing north along the well-graded, main road, which is Forest Road 153. Travel eighteen and six-tenths miles to the Blue Spruce Campground where, if desired, you can rest and/or spend the night. As you travel, be sure to stop from time to time and explore some of the countryside, since quality agate and jasper can be found just about anywhere along this stretch. At the campground, there is a very faint trail leading to a productive agate and jasper bed about one-half mile to the north. This is Site B and it features beautiful bright red jasper. The hike isn't difficult and the location is conducive to a leisurely walk. Just take your time and enjoy the scenery.

To get to Site C, either continue on Forest Road 153, as shown on the map, or return to Highway 12. Head northeast on Highway 12 about twenty-three miles, turn left onto Hell's Backbone Road (Forest Road 153), and go about five more miles to the collecting site. The agate and jasper is so brilliantly red here that you can actually see it among the pine needles from your vehicle as you travel. The collecting extends for at least another mile along the road and for quite a distance among the trees on either side.

Parked at Site C

HELL'S BACKBONE

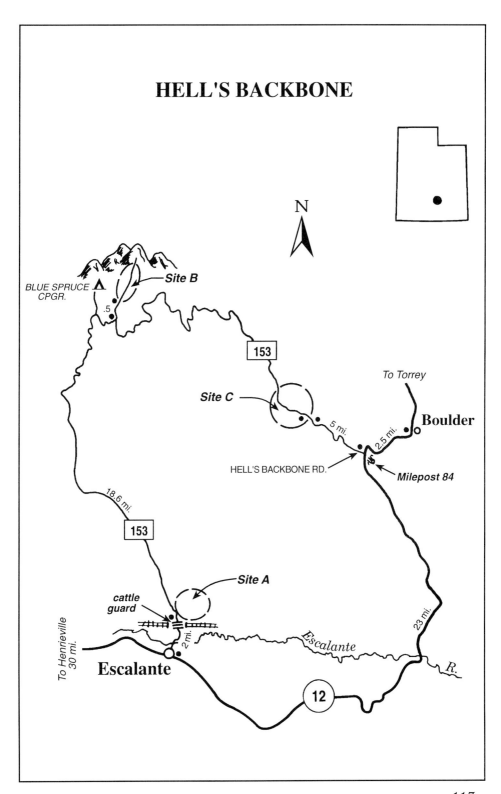

N

BLUE SPRUCE CPGR.

Site B

.5

153

To Torrey

Site C

5 mi.

2.5 mi.

Boulder

HELL'S BACKBONE RD.

Milepost 84

18.6 mi.

153

Site A

cattle guard

2 mi.

Escalante

23 mi.

To Henrieville 30 mi.

Escalante

R.

12

This is a great place to find petrified wood, but it requires a steep hike and, therefore, should only be tackled by collectors in good physical condition. There are some very washed out ruts which lead through the center of the site, and a high-clearance, four-wheel drive unit might be able to make it. That decision, however, is up to you.

To get there, go west from Escalante, on Highway 12, one and nine-tenths miles. At that point, there is a faint road on the left. Drive as far as you can, which will probably be only about one-tenth of a mile, and park.

Hike along the eroded ruts as they go up the hill thorough the brush. Wood can be found over an extensive area, starting about one mile from the highway. You should try to explore as much of the region as possible. Very large pieces can be obtained, as well as lots of smaller material, most of which is specimen quality, but isn't solid enough to take a good polish. This has long been a known rockhounding spot and regions near the road have been heavily picked over. To get anything worthwhile, some hiking away from the road will be required.

While in the area, be sure to visit the Escalante Petrified Forest on the opposite side of Highway 12 only two-tenths of a mile back toward town.

There, you will find a small lake, camping facilities, and a well-marked nature trail which takes you through a forest of petrified logs. There is a vehicle entry fee but the cost is worth it. Obviously, no collecting is allowed with-in the park boundaries, but that material is almost identical to what can be found at the collecting site.

Samples of petrified wood discovered near Escalante

ESCALANTE

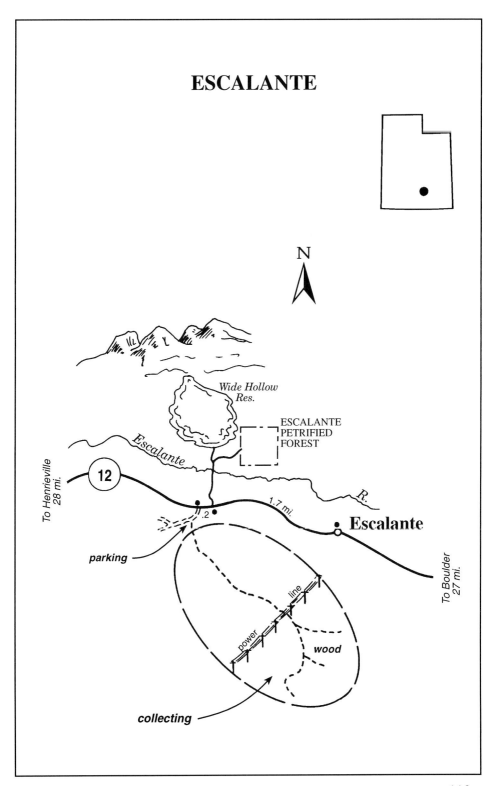

N

Wide Hollow
Res.

ESCALANTE
PETRIFIED
FOREST

Escalante

12

To Henrieville
28 mi.

1.7 mi.

.2

R.

Escalante

parking

To Boulder
27 mi.

power   line

wood

collecting

This vast collecting area might frustrate some rockhounds because of its magnitude and the lack of an exact, pinpointed spot on which to collect. Drive four and one-half miles east from Escalante on Highway 12, turn south onto the road to Hole-In-The-Rock, and continue seventeen miles to the Garfield/Kane County line. At that point, you will be at the site's northern boundary. From there, extending south another thirty-three miles, lots of quality agate and petrified wood can be found in the foothills of massive Straight Cliffs, which parallel the road, on the west.

Follow any of the ruts which head toward the imposing cliffs and attempt to get as close as possible. From where you must stop, it will then be necessary to hike the rest of the way. Pay particularly close attention to the debris that has crumbled from high above, as well as areas of erosion. Be sure to also look for partially buried wood sticking out from the side of the cliffs. Huge logs can be found here, and what might appear on the surface as a small chunk could actually turn out to be an incredibly large (and impossible to remove) petrified tree trunk! If you choose to dig on the cliffs, BE VERY CAREFUL, not only for yourself, but for others who might be down below, because some of the soil is very unstable.

Since most collectors tend to only explore the northern portion of the collecting site, due to its proximity to Escalante, driving farther south might place you in more virgin terrain. Keep in mind that this is a collecting area that requires a desire to do some exploring. If you don't find much on your first try, drive a little farther, head in toward the cliffs, and try again.

View of the cliffs at the collecting area

STRAIGHT CLIFFS

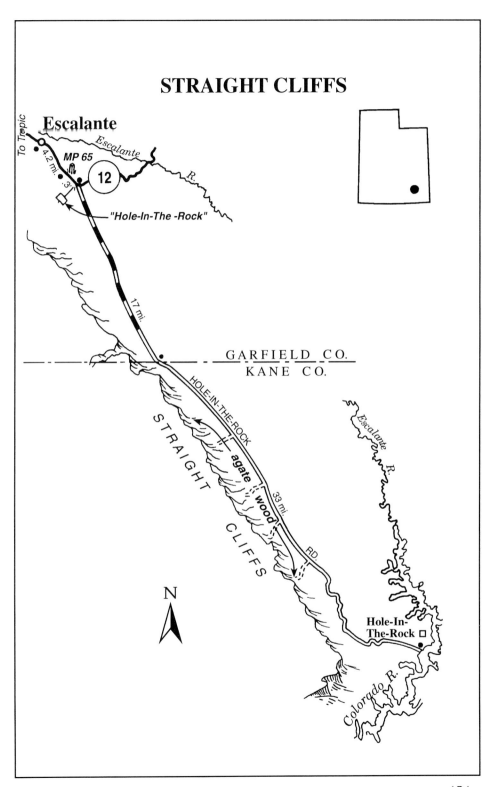

Escalante

To Tropic

Escalante R.

MP 65

4.2 mi.

.3

12

"Hole-In-The -Rock"

17 mi.

GARFIELD CO.
KANE CO.

HOLE-IN-THE-ROCK

S T R A I G H T

agate

wood

33 mi.

RD.

C L I F F S

Escalante R.

N

Hole-In-
The-Rock □

Colorado R.

These two sites offer a good opportunity to gather quality red agate and even some unusual coprolite. To get to Site A, the coprolite spot, go twenty and one-half miles south from Hanksville on Highway 95 and turn onto the graded, dirt road which heads west. Continue three and nine-tenths miles to Little Egypt, where you should stop and view the unusually shaped geological formations.

From Little Egypt, continue on the main road, bearing right at the first fork and left at the next. The latter is encountered just after passing through a wash. From there, the road starts to deteriorate, but most rugged vehicles should have no trouble. Go another five and one-half miles, bearing left at each of the two major forks, as shown on the map. At that point, you will be on a flat area overlooking a deep canyon. Hunt the region to the right of the road for the coprolite. The sometimes colorful, petrified dinosaur dung is not overly plentiful anymore, but, for some reason, there seems to have been a lot of it deposited here. It is generally quite easy to identify, due to its somewhat distinctive appearance.

To get to Site B, return to Highway 95 and go south another six miles, bearing onto Highway 276. The turnoff is on the right, just after you get onto Highway 276. From there, proceed west three and one-tenth miles to where agate can be found scattered all over the ground, primarily to the south. The collecting extends south for at least two miles and there are some washed out ruts which parallel the mountains in that direction.

LITTLE EGYPT

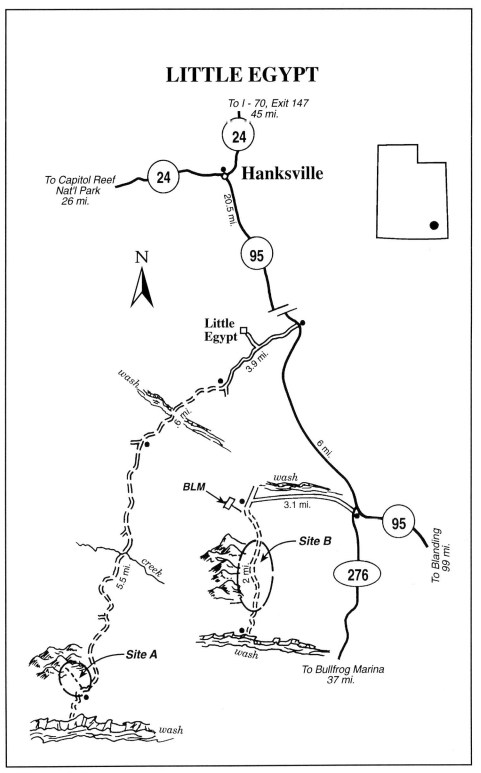

To I - 70, Exit 147
45 mi.

24

24

To Capitol Reef
Nat'l Park
26 mi.

Hanksville

20.5 mi.

95

N

Little
Egypt

3.9 mi.

wash

6.9 mi.

6 mi.

wash

BLM

3.1 mi.

95

To Blanding
99 mi.

Site B

2 mi.

creek

5.5 mi.

276

Site A

wash

To Bullfrog Marina
37 mi.

wash

These five sites boast an excellent variety of colorful agate, as well as top quality jasper, alabaster, and calcite. Each site is worth visiting if you have a vehicle capable of navigating the sometimes challenging roads.

To get to the first, go east twelve miles from the bridge over the Green River on Interstate 70 and take Exit 173. Follow the graded, dirt road as it heads south for five and four-tenths miles, and then proceed east one-half mile to Site A. There, you will find agate scattered all over, and most is very nice, tending to be white, red and orange. The prize, however, at this and the other locations, is the pigeon blood material, a brilliant white filled with blood red "droplets." Chunks of petrified wood can also be picked up.

To get to Site B, return to the main road and go only two-tenths of a mile farther south to where ruts intersect on the left. Follow them for one mile, as they go along the north side of the old corral into the shallow hills. Here, as was the case at Site A, you will find lots of agate scattered about.

Site C is reached by returning to the main road, going two-tenths of a mile more, and this time following the ruts nine-tenths of a mile around the south side of the old corral. En route you will pass through a series of washes, but most rugged vehicles should be able to make it. At the given mileage, agate can be found all over, especially on the hill to the right of the road.

Site D is located one and four-tenths miles farther on the main road. Just before crossing a major wash, there are some ruts paralleling it. Follow those ruts about five and one-half miles, as they enter and exit the sandy wash. At the given mileage, there are some hills on the right and it is in and around those hills where you can find alabaster, calcite, multi-colored jasper, and some very nice red, yellow, blue and white agate.

To get to Site E, return to the main road and proceed south another two and six-tenths miles. There, intersecting from the west, are some ruts which you should follow a little more than three very rough miles to the start of the collecting site, which is at the top of a little hill overlooking a wash. From the top of the hill and into the wash there are digging holes left by previous gem hunters where one can find lots of very colorful jasper, primarily in shades of yellow, red and tan.

Camping at Site B

GREEN RIVER

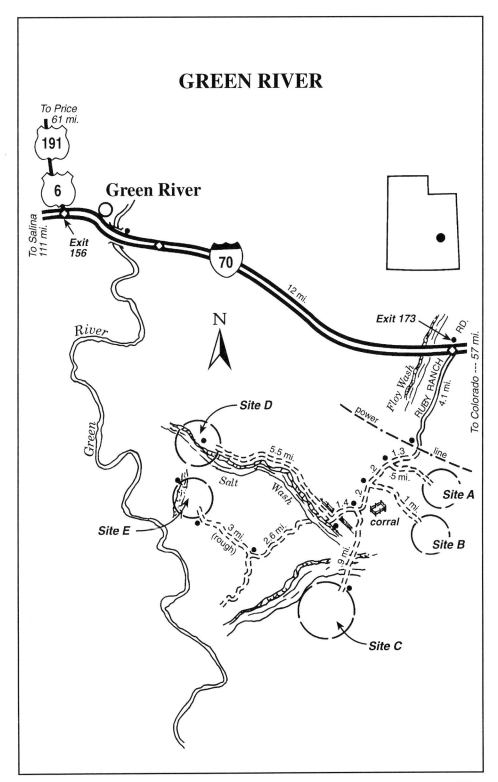

Very nice agate and an occasional septarium nodule can be found near Burro Seep, only a few miles south of Crescent Junction. To reach the collecting area, start where Highway 191 intersects Interstate 70, at Exit 180, about nineteen miles east of Green River. From there, go south on Highway 191 fifteen and two-tenths miles and turn east toward Seep Spring. If you miss the turnoff, just continue south to Highway 313 and double back five and seven-tenths miles, as shown on the map. You will pass through a range fence shortly after leaving the highway, and it should be left as found after passing through.

Continue one and six-tenths miles, bear right at the fork, and go another two and one-half miles to where some dim ruts intersect from the right. Follow those rough tracks another two-tenths of a mile. If you are not sure your vehicle can make this last short stretch, simply park off the main road and hike. The collecting begins approximately where the ruts cross the wash and continue throughout the hills and lowlands for quite a distance.

Lots of colorful agate in shades of white, red and maroon can be found here, especially if you are willing to do some hiking away from the most accessible regions. The septarium nodules are much more difficult to find,

however. Search for them in areas of erosion in or near the hills. Once you find one, try to determine where it originally came from. Was it washed down the hillside or is it being weathered directly from the deposit itself? If you can determine the source, some digging with pick and shovel might provide additional and better quality nodules. Obviously, a certain amount of luck will also be needed.

Searching for agate and septarium nodules

CRESCENT JUNCTION

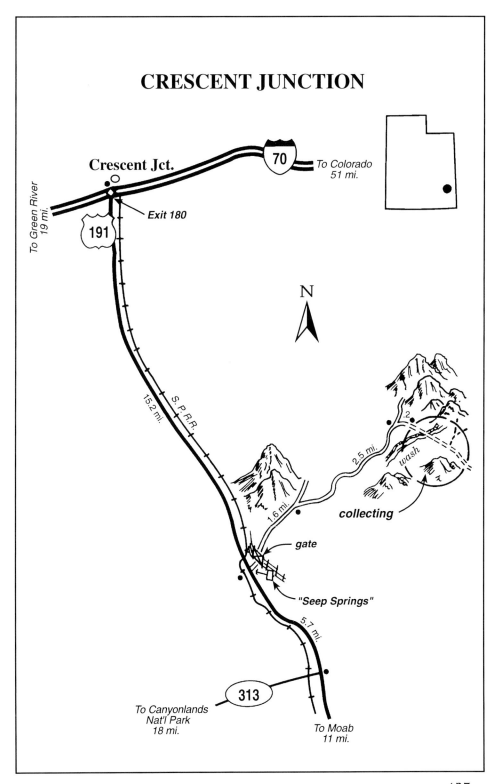

Crescent Jct.

70 To Colorado 51 mi.

To Green River 19 mi.

191

Exit 180

N

15.2 mi.

S. P. R.R.

2.5 mi.

wash

collecting

1.6 mi.

gate

"Seep Springs"

5.7 mi.

313

To Canyonlands Nat'l Park 18 mi.

To Moab 11 mi.

This location offers lots of agate and is situated in one of the most scenic parts of Utah. To get there, proceed south seven-tenths of a mile from La Sal Junction, on Highway 191, to Looking Glass Road. Turn right, go one-half mile, and again turn right. Shortly after making the last turn, agate can be found on both sides of the road for quite a distance. The best and largest chunks tend to be on the upper slopes of the little hill, about one-half mile away.

On that hill, there are remnants of an old corral, but very little is left. Search the surrounding terrain, continuing to the opposite slopes. It doesn't take long to gather a substantial amount of agate, but most is white and relatively uninteresting.

To get the finest this spot has to offer, it is necessary to spend some time carefully examining everything picked up. Some material contains fascinating black moss and dendritic inclusions, as well as regions of brilliant color. The most prized agate from here is that with deep red regions contrasting vividly with the host white. Such pieces, if cut properly, can produce incredible cabochons.

While in the area, be sure to continue along the main road to see Looking Glass Rock. In addition, Newspaper Rock, about thirty miles farther south, is also worth the visit. There, you will see a large overhang protecting innumerable ancient petroglyphs on the side of a cliff.

Road through part of the collecting area

LOOKING GLASS ROAD

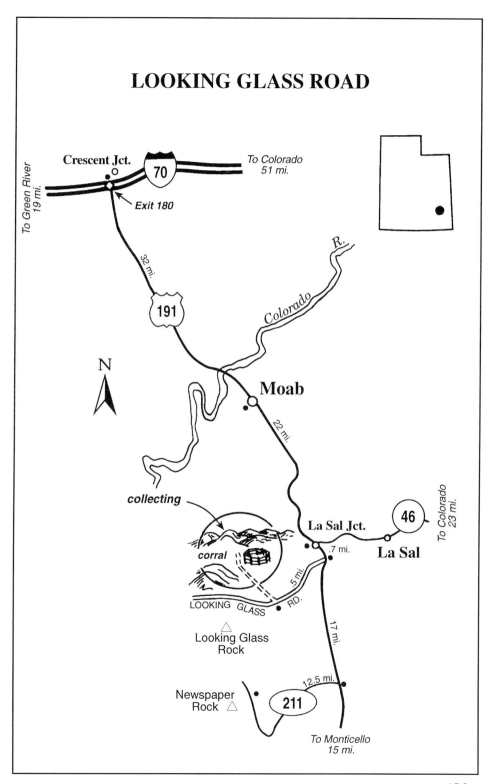

Joe Wilson Canyon and the wash running through it are noted for the fine agate that can be found there. To get to the main collecting site, take Highway 191 twenty-two miles south from Moab to La Sal Junction. From there, continue another four and three-tenths miles to where a bridge crosses the wash. There is a flat place to park on the southeast side of the bridge, but the soil is somewhat soft and that could present problems for some vehicles. Park where you think is best, but be sure you are well off the pavement.

Scant amounts of agate can be found alongside the highway near the bridge, but the best and largest pieces are obtained by hiking through the sandy creekbed. The trek isn't difficult and a faint trail can be seen leading down from the highway. After walking about one-fourth of a mile, the agate chunks tend to get larger, with material being randomly scattered throughout the wash and on the surrounding banks. Sizes range from small pebbles to boulders, and it occurs in a variety of colors, including red, maroon, purple and blue, most of which is in combination with white. Agate with more than one color is very nice, if not internally fractured, and can be used to make outstanding polished pieces.

Since this locality is so easily accessible, supplies have become more and more depleted over the years. It seems that each year the rains do uncover and/or wash more material down from the deposits. Now, if you want much success, it usually takes more time, effort, and hiking.

The creekbed running through the site

130

LA SAL JUNCTION

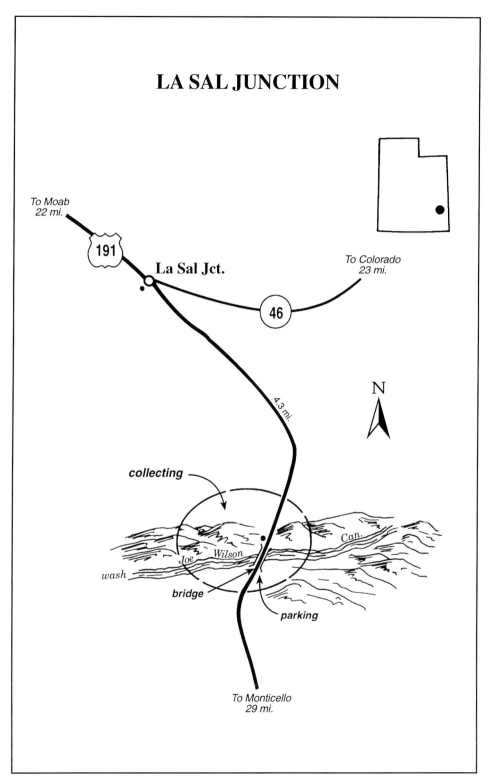

To Moab
22 mi.

191

La Sal Jct.

To Colorado
23 mi.

46

4.3 mi.

N

collecting

Can.

Joe Wilson

wash

bridge

parking

To Monticello
29 mi.

There are many agate deposits in the region surrounding Moab, but this site is one of the most extensive. Take Highway 191 south from Moab twenty miles to the large pumping station. From there, continue only one-half mile farther, turn left onto the dirt road, and go another six-tenths of a mile. At that point, some tracks intersect on the left, and you should follow them seven-tenths of a mile to a little wash which is in the center of the collecting area.

Agate can be found throughout the hills surrounding the wash, as well as in the wash itself. Sizes range from tiny pieces, suitable only for tumbling, to small boulders. Most of the agate is white, but some contain interesting inclusions. Other colors can also be found, including blue, tan, gray, red and orange. The other hues are usually mixed with the white, producing very nice specimens. Chunks with deep blood red regions, contrasting brilliantly with the clean, bright white, are the most highly prized. Such material can be used to make excellent cabochons and other polished pieces. Much of the rock in this area is covered with dried mud, so you may have to split any suspect stones in order to identify and determine quality.

This is a huge site, extending for many miles from the wash, in all directions, so be sure to explore regions a distance from the road. Usually, places that take some effort to get to afford better chances for finding larger quantities of the best material. Since this is a lightly forested area, be sure you don't wander too far and become disoriented.

The road to the collecting site

MOAB

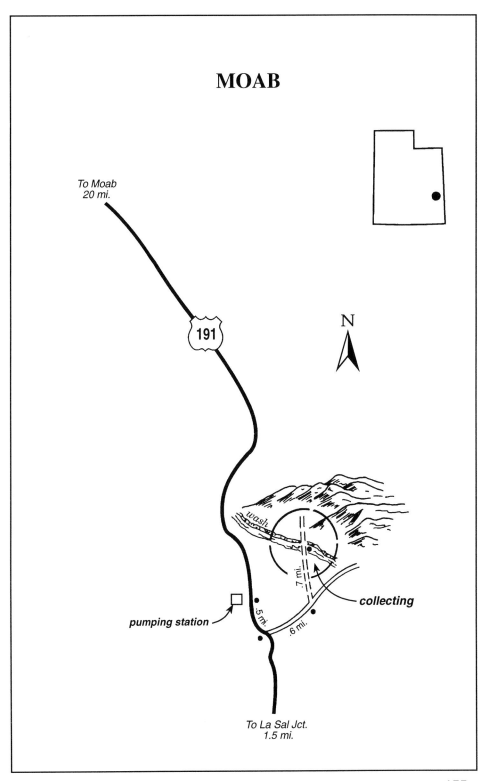

To Moab
20 mi.

191

N

wash

.7 mi.

pumping station

.5 mi.

.6 mi.

collecting

To La Sal Jct.
1.5 mi.

These two sites feature red and white agate, ranging in size from chips to pieces with dimensions of many inches. The quality tends to be excellent, and that with rich red and white mixed together is the most highly prized and ardently sought.

To reach Site A, go eight and two-tenths miles west on Highway 313 from where it intersects Highway 191. At that point, turn right toward Dubinky Well. Follow the graded, dirt road one and four-tenths miles and turn right on the ruts leading onto a low flat area one and four-tenths miles away. The last stretch is somewhat rough, but should be no problem for most vehicles.

The agate is scattered throughout the limestone which covers most of the mesa. It is found all over the upper regions and the lower slopes, in varying concentrations of color and quality, so be sure to take enough time to adequately explore the entire area to assure that you find the best the site has to offer.

To get to Site B, return to Dubinky Well Road and go northwest an additional two and three-tenth miles to a cattle guard. From there, and extending quite a distance on both sides of the road, one can find more agate scattered throughout the surrounding countryside. Most of the material that occurs here is white, but some red, blue and tan material can also be found.

Probably, both of these sites are actually just portions of a single extensive agate field, and, if you have the time, it might be worthwhile exploring the terrain between them.

Searching for agate at Site A

DUBINKY WELL

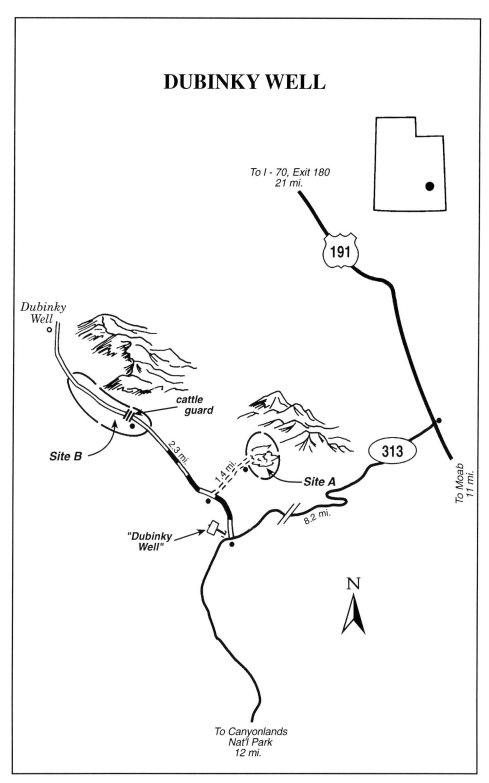

To I - 70, Exit 180
21 mi.

191

Dubinky
Well

cattle
guard

Site B

2.3 mi.

1.4 mi.

Site A

313

To Moab
11 mi.

"Dubinky
Well"

8.2 mi.

N

To Canyonlands
Nat'l Park
12 mi.

Each of the four different sites illustrated on the accompanying map will take you to an interesting and potentially productive collecting area. To get to Site A, drive ten miles south from Cisco on Highway 128. From there, and continuing all the way to the Colorado River, on both sides of the road, you can find agate. Park off the pavement and search the flatlands and hills. If you don't find much at your first stop go a little farther and try again.

To reach Site B, proceed north to Interstate 70, drive west eleven miles to Exit 191, and turn south on the graded, dirt road. Drive five and eight-tenths miles, turn right, following the ruts past the ruins two and eight-tenths miles. Then go right again, continuing another two and one-tenth miles. That last stretch is very rough and, if wet, probably impassable unless you have four-wheel drive.

At the given mileage, you will be near an orange butte, which marks the start of this vast collecting area. Look for agate, jasper, petrified wood and interesting agate pseudomorphs after barite. Material can be found on both sides of the road for at least another mile. The agate is generally pastel, but some nice carnelian pieces can also be obtained. The pseudomorphs are especially desirable, resembling pine cones or clusters of grapes. Some material has a deep red interior which, when cut, exhibits a fascinating, radiating, internal structure. Pay particularly close attention to washes and other areas of erosion for the best specimens.

Return to the main road and travel one and six-tenths miles farther south and then left for three and eight-tenth miles, bearing left at the fork, to Site D. Here, more agate can be found on the slopes. The road into the hills is very rough and four-wheel drive will probably be necessary.

The final collecting spot, Site C, is extensive. The northern boundary is reached by going south on the main road seven-tenths of a mile from where the Site D road intersected. Starting there, and continuing at least one more

mile, you should be able to find jasper, gypsum crystals, barite balls, petrified wood, dinosaur bone, and even the occasional arrowhead.

Site B

CISCO AND YELLOW CAT

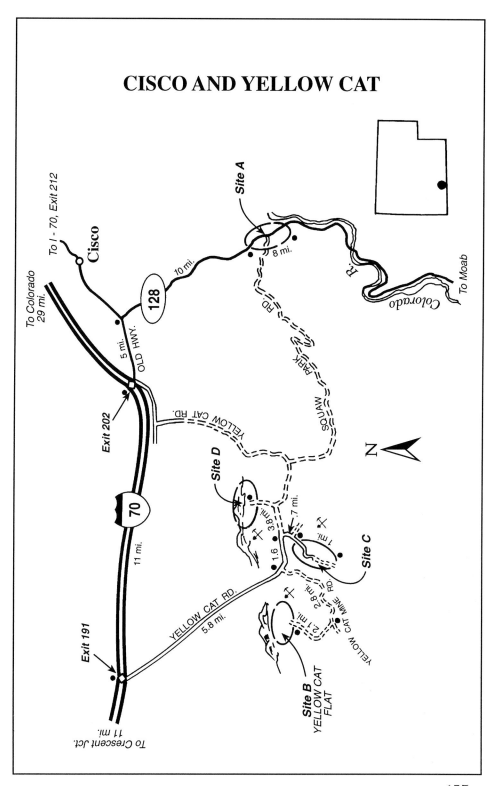

137

A good variety of minerals can be found at these two sites, both of which are fairly easy to get to. For Site A, head south on Highway 24 seven-tenths of a mile from Exit 147, on Interstate 70. Turn right and drive to the mounds north of the road, about two-tenths of a mile farther. A very short distance past the hills is a highway department facility and no trespassing is allowed there.

Search the flatlands stretching toward Interstate 70, as well as the hills themselves. You can pick up small amounts of agate, an occasional chunk of grape agate, jasper and even some chips of petrified wood. An unusual conglomerate jasper can also be found here, some of which produces incredibly colorful polished pieces if the cementing agent is solid. This location has been known for quite a few years and, due to its easy accessibility, most of the surface material has been removed. Top quality chunks are few and far between, so don't expect massive amounts of anything.

Site B is by far the more prolific of the two locations and is reached by returning to Highway 24 and driving south three and one-half more miles. From there, follow the ruts leading east from the pavement one additional mile. You will pass through a series of washes, so be very sure your vehicle can make it. At the given mileage, scattered throughout the surrounding hills, is petrified wood, agate, jasper, dinosaur bone, coprolite, selenite and even some nice spherical concretions. Pay particularly close attention to the colorful mounds on the left side of the road. Digging into that soft soil might expose additional material. Inspecting areas of erosion and doing some walking usually produces plenty of specimens without the hard work.

A view of collecting Site B

SAN RAFAEL

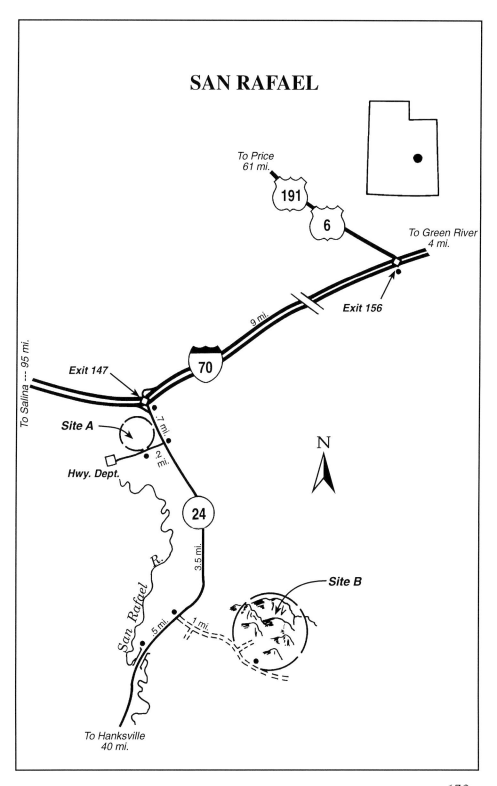

To Price
61 mi.

191

6

To Green River
4 mi.

Exit 156

9 mi.

To Salina --- 95 mi.

Exit 147

70

Site A

.7 mi.

.2 mi.

Hwy. Dept.

N

24

3.5 mi.

San Rafael R.

Site B

.5 mi.

1 mi.

To Hanksville
40 mi.

This location offers a good variety of interesting collectables. The list includes colorful agate, petrified wood, and even some fossilized dinosaur bone. To get to there, take Exit 156 from Interstate 70 and head north on Highway 6/191. Go about sixteen miles to where the Castle Dale Road intersects from the west. There is a sign at the intersection, so be on the lookout. From there, pass under the railroad tracks and proceed three miles toward Castle Dale to the southeastern edge of the collecting area.

Just park off the main road and hike to the northwest, keeping a keen eye to the ground. The agate is fairly easy to spot, since it looks almost white from a distance, thereby contrasting nicely against the darker surrounding soil. Just about any white appearing rock you encounter will probably be agate. To best ascertain whether or not it is worth keeping, it might be necessary to split it with a rock pick in order to view a fresh, unabraided and unweathered surface, which better displays the internal color and inclusion content. The most prized of the Summerville Wash agate is a brilliant red material, sometimes associated with nice contrasting regions of black. Lighter colors are also available, but the red, especially if fairly transparent, is stunning.

The wood tends to occur in shades of tan and light brown, while the dinosaur bone is primarily tan and very scarce. If you don't find much at your first stop, continue a half mile or so toward Castle Dale and try again. The field is at least a mile in diameter and mineral concentration does vary.

SUMMERVILLE WASH

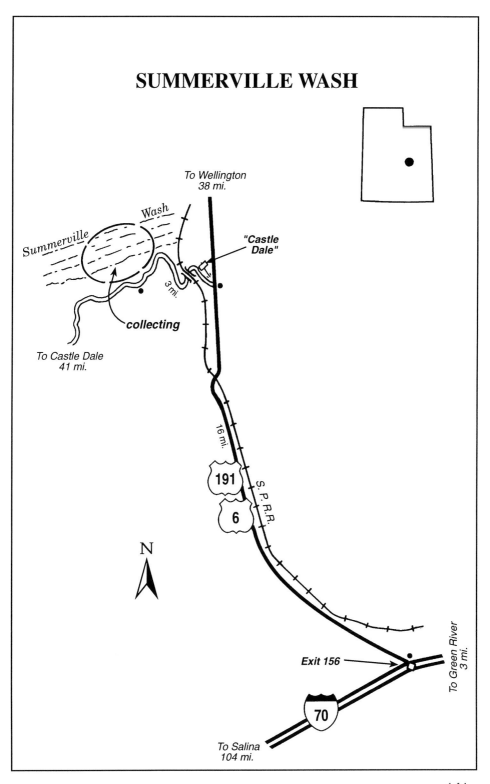

To Wellington
38 mi.

Summerville Wash

"Castle
Dale"

3 mi.

collecting

To Castle Dale
41 mi.

16 mi.

191

6

S.P.R.R.

N

Exit 156

To Green River
3 mi.

70

To Salina
104 mi.

*Parked at Site B at the
San Rafael collecting site*

*Searching for agate at the
Looking Glass Road site*

INTRODUCTION TO SUPPLEMENTAL LOCATIONS: PART II

The following sites are not described in Part I, primarily because the author has not yet had a chance to personally visit them or they may be so vast that no exact spot could be pinpointed for good mineral concentration. Each, however, has been supplied and verified by reliable sources and affords excellent collecting opportunities. Be sure to follow all of the cautions and suggestions discussed in the Introduction. These sites will provide you with a chance to see additional scenic and geologically interesting portions of Utah, as well as give you an opportunity to obtain some fine minerals.

It is hoped that the supplemental locations put a sense of exploration and adventure into your tour of this fascinating and beautiful state. So many of the more popular collecting localities are either closed, over regulated, or slowly being depleted, with much of their finest material having been removed long ago. That is less likely to have happened with these spots. If you are patient and flexible, with a willingness to put out a little extra effort, they could very well be a highlight of your rockhounding trip.

The two locations shown on the accompanying map provide collectors with the opportunity to gather some interesting Lower Ordovician Period fossils. These include trilobites, brachiopods, cephalopods and gastropods (snails). To get to Site A, go about fifty-three miles west from Delta on Highway 6/50 to the Tule Valley Road turnoff. Proceed south ten and two-tenths miles and then go right another two miles on Blind Valley Road.

At that point, to the north, are cliffs within which can be seen the gray, fossil-bearing limestone which marks the collecting site. Park well off the road and hike to the deposit. Try to allow plenty of time to adequately explore the numerous layers of limestone, keeping in mind that lower layers can provide very different types of specimens than those farther up.

If you don't have the initiative and or energy to attack the tough limestone directly in the cliffs, lots of fossil-bearing rock can be found below, having been weathered away. Take any suspicious block of limestone and, using a chisel and hammer, start splitting. The shells are easy to find, but the trilobites are much more rare. This is not only due to the fact that they are tougher to spot and more sparsely distributed, but they are also confined to a relatively small portion of the limestone layering.

Site B is accessed by continuing west on Blind Valley Road another two and two-tenths miles and then going right four-tenths of a mile. At that point, some rough tracks will be spotted leading off to the left. Those tracks lead to what is locally referred to as Fossil Mountain. As was the case at Site A, the fossils occur within the layers of limestone and shale which are easily spotted from below, and each layer has the potential to provide differing types of ancient sea-life. Search Fossil Mountain in the same way suggested for Site A.

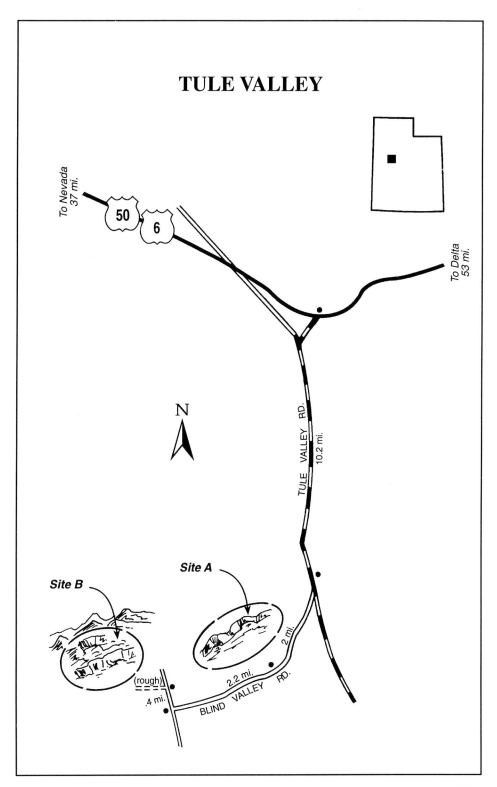

TULE VALLEY

To Nevada 37 mi.

50 6

To Delta 53 mi.

N

TULE VALLEY RD. 10.2 mi.

Site A

Site B

(rough)

.4 mi.

2.2 mi.

2 mi.

BLIND VALLEY RD.

At one time, beautiful black and white agate was mined in the hills marking the center of this collecting site. That, however, was nearly one-half century ago, and, since then, all traces of the prospect have been obscured by the forces of nature. Chips can still be found, as can an occasional tumbling sized pebble, but pieces large enough to be cut and fashioned into cabochons are few and far between. If, however, you have the time and the willingness to do some searching and digging, you may be able to rediscover the agate-bearing seams and procure some great material.

To get there, head south on Highway 28 from Levan about twelve and one-half miles. The turnoff is very difficult to spot, especially when traveling south, so, if you get to the Juab/Sanpete County line, you have gone too far and should double back about two-tenths of a mile to the dim tracks leading east from the pavement. Do not turn at the first and easier spotted road, but go to the second. Proceed about two-tenths of a mile, passing through a gate which should be reclosed after being driven through. Turn left onto the old highway, now little more than a bumpy dirt road with occasional patches of asphalt showing. Continue another one-half mile to where remnants of an old corral can be seen on the right side of the road and follow the tracks leading east, down the hill, past that corral.

Chips of the black and white agate will be spotted after having gone only a few tenths of a mile, but go about eight-tenths of a mile before stopping. From there, search throughout the little hills and pay particularly close attention to areas of erosion. As mentioned earlier, chips and small specimens are not too tough to find, but, if you want to locate the actual source, patient exploration and careful examination of the surrounding hills will be needed.

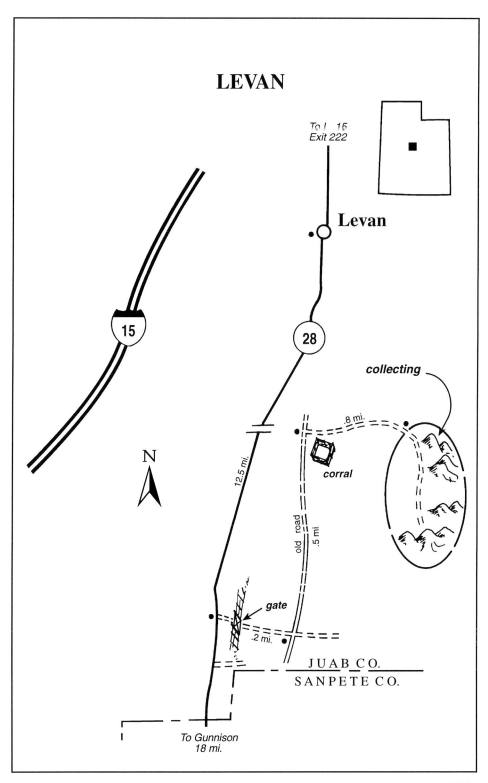

LEVAN

To I-15
Exit 222

Levan

15

28

collecting

.8 mi.

corral

12.5 mi.

old road

.5 mi.

N

gate

.2 mi.

JUAB CO.
SANPETE CO.

To Gunnison
18 mi.

The once bustling town of Gold Hill is not exactly situated in a major population center. In fact, it is downright remote, but the mineral collecting potential offered by the many mine dumps in the surrounding hills might make the effort to get there worthwhile.

If you are interested, start in Wendover, Nevada, just west of the Utah/ Nevada border, on Interstate 80. At Exit 410, go south on Alternate Highway 93 for twenty-six miles, turn left, driving another sixteen miles, and then left again onto the well-graded, dirt road for the final twelve miles. As you approach, old dumps will be spotted in the surrounding hills, and any of them offer collecting potential. The problem, however, is getting to them. Old roads might get you close, if you have four-wheel drive and/or a rugged, high-clearance vehicle. To reach most, however, you will still have to do some walking.

The dumps boast lots of nice specimens, and, because of the site's remoteness, there seems to be good material still readily available. Malachite, azurite, austinite, cuproadamite, chrysocolla, galena, pyrite, bornite, orpiment, realgar, and smithsonite are just a few of the many minerals that have been found throughout the Gold Hill region dumps. Be advised that the beautiful orange and reds of the arsenic ores orpiment and realgar are potentially hazardous. If you do collect any of those minerals, be certain to thoroughly wash your hands before eating, since the arsenic could make you quite sick.

If you don't have access to a four-wheel drive vehicle, don't worry. The roads leading to Gold Hill are passable, even in a passenger car, and some of the dumps are only a short hike from a decent road. As is always the case when collecting at old prospects, be certain wherever you choose to go is open. Do not trespass. Be also advised that this region can get scorching hot during the summer months, making it a much better spring and fall locality.

GOLD HILL

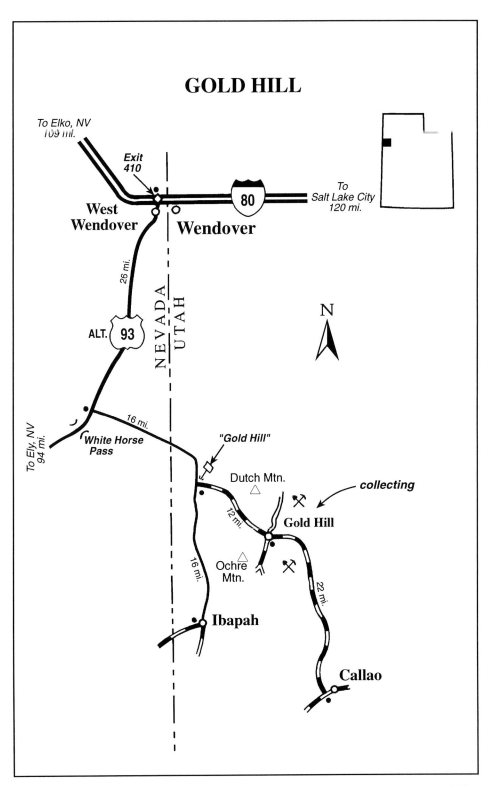

Calcite, fluorite, galena, quartz, garnet, pyrolusite, cerussite, feldspar and biotite are just a few of the many minerals that can be found in the dumps scattered throughout the areas illustrated on the accompanying map.

To get to Region A, travel about thirty-five miles west from Milford on Highway 21 to milepost 42. At that point, turn south toward Lund, go four and one-half miles to a major intersection, and continue straight ahead another ten miles. Mine dumps will be seen scattered throughout the surrounding hills for quite a distance and any of them offers good collecting potential. The roads leading to those dumps are often quite rough or completely washed out, however, so four-wheel drive is most important if you want to get close without being forced to take a long hike. Be very careful, even with four-wheel drive, to not get yourself in a dangerous situation, since this is a very remote area and help is many miles of desolate road away.

Be certain to also make sure whichever dump(s) you choose to explore are abandoned and open to collecting. Do not trespass. Nice yellow andradite garnet is the mineral most frequently sought in Region A, but keep your eye out for others.

To get to Region B, return to Pine Valley Wash Road, as shown on the map, turn right, and drive another eighteen miles to Fisher Wash Road. There is a sign designating it to be the route to Cougar Spar and Indian Peak. Go right approximately ten miles to the Indian Peak Wildlife Management Area turnoff, that intersection marks the center of Region B. As was the case before, the hills are littered with old prospects, and you should search any that are abandoned. Minerals of primary interest within these dumps include nice calcite, quartz, galena and fluorite crystals, as well as specimens of cerussite, pyrolusite and a delicately colored yellow variety of andradite garnet.

SAWTOOTH PEAK

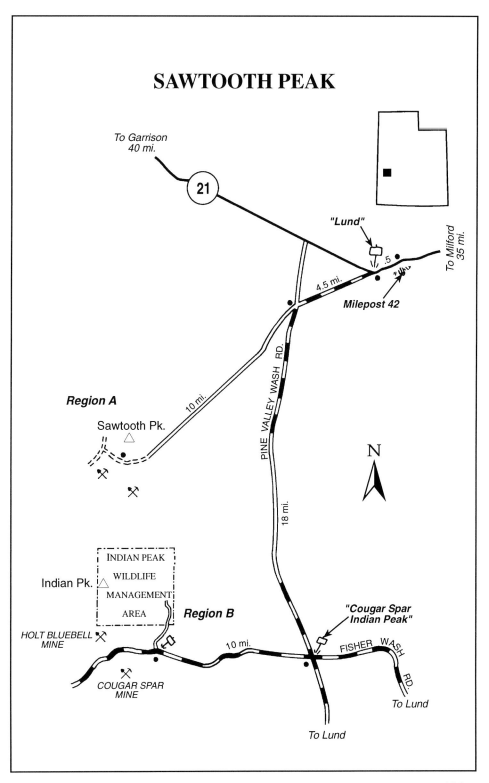

To Garrison
40 mi.

21

"Lund"

To Milford
35 mi.

.5

4.5 mi.

Milepost 42

PINE VALLEY WASH RD.

Region A

Sawtooth Pk.

10 mi.

N

18 mi.

INDIAN PEAK
WILDLIFE
MANAGEMENT
AREA

Indian Pk.

Region B

"Cougar Spar
Indian Peak"

HOLT BLUEBELL
MINE

10 mi.

FISHER WASH

RD.

To Lund

COUGAR SPAR
MINE

To Lund

To Lund

Agate can be gathered in and around a group of little hills located about one hundred miles southwest of Hanksville. To get there, go southwest on Highway 276 for about twenty miles from where it intersects Highway 95. As you start to climb out of the flatlands onto the southeast slopes of Clay Hills, there will be a cattle guard across the pavement.

About one-tenth of a mile past that cattle guard is a very rough road leading off to the left which will take you through the center of the collecting site. Follow it about one-half mile and park just about anywhere from that point, continuing at least another one-half mile. Hike in any direction through the surrounding countryside.

Be advised that the road leading through the collecting site is only passable with a high-clearance, rugged, four-wheel drive unit. In fact, even if you have such a vehicle, you still might have some problems. It might be a good idea to park beside the highway and simply hike.

The agate is fairly easy to spot, since it contrasts nicely against the darker soil. Some of the material is very colorful and contains intricate moss-like inclusions, while other pieces are relatively uninteresting. When you find a good-sized chunk, it is usually helpful to break off a portion with a rock pick in order to better determine its desirability. It is always easier to tell a stone's quality by examining a freshly exposed surface rather than a weathered and soiled one. If you don't have much luck at your first stop, continue along the ruts a little farther and try again.

CLAY HILLS

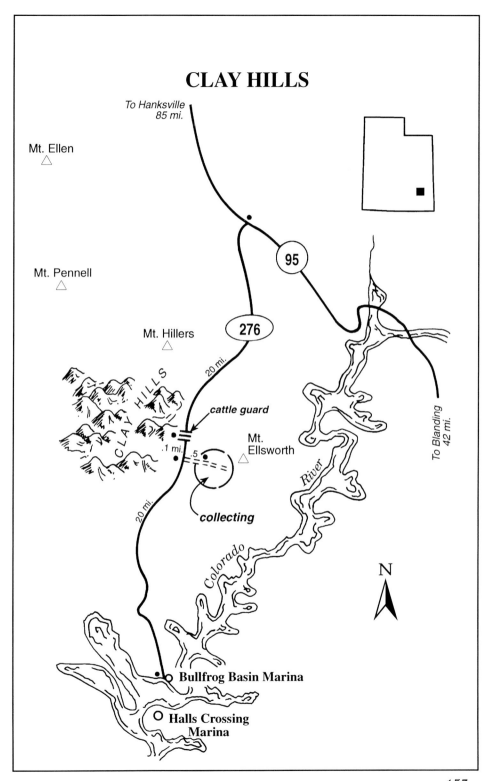

To Hanksville
85 mi.

Mt. Ellen

Mt. Pennell

95

Mt. Hillers

276

20 mi.

CLAY HILLS

cattle guard

.1 mi.   .5

Mt. Ellsworth

collecting

20 mi.

Colorado River

N

Bullfrog Basin Marina

Halls Crossing Marina

To Blanding
42 mi.

The region surrounding Escalante and Boulder is well known for its abundant supply of petrified wood. In fact, even if you randomly stop along the highway, it would not be surprising to find a piece just lying there, right next to the pavement. There are, however, a few locations that are more reliable and productive, one of which is Egg Canyon.

To get there, take the Burr Trail east out of Boulder, as illustrated on the map, and travel about ten and one-half miles to The Gulch, which has become a popular recreation site. Proceed another twelve and one-half miles to where a BLM sign notes the turnoff to The Lampstand, among other things. It is there where you should leave the Burr Trail and head northwest. From that point, there are quite a number of intersecting roads, and you must try to remain on the main one as it curves westward to the south of prominent Circle Cliffs.

About eight and three-tenths miles from the Burr Trail you should encounter a major fork, and the remnants of an old corral. At that fork, bear left and proceed another two miles to road's end, which is where you must park. From there, it is necessary to trek over the ridge and down the other side into Egg Canyon.

Search the wash area and surrounding terrain for the dark brown wood. Lots of the specimens are somewhat porous, and thereby incapable of taking a good polish. Other pieces are very solid and some specimens contain beautiful patches and streaks of brilliant orange and red. Even the porous material is worth keeping if it displays the wood structure well enough, but just remember that all you find must be carried back. That fact will greatly influence your selectivity. If dissatisfied with what can be found on the surface, look for pits where previous collectors have worked. If you have the energy, some heavy pick and shovel work in promising areas might turn up some real prizes.

EGG CANYON

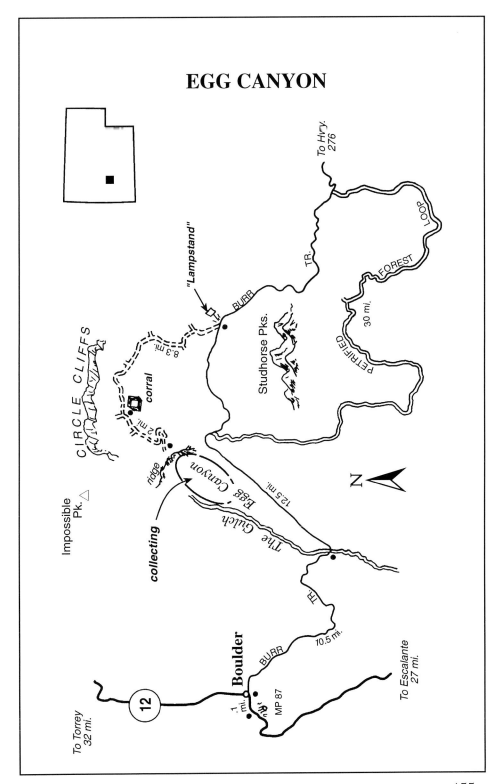

To Hwy. 276

LOOP

FOREST

PETRIFIED

30 mi.

"Lampstand"

BURR   TR.

Studhorse Pks.

CIRCLE CLIFFS

8.3 mi.

corral

2 mi.

ridge

collecting

Impossible Pk. △

Egg Canyon

The Gulch

12.5 mi.

N

Boulder

BURR

10.5 mi.

MP 87

12

To Torrey 32 mi.

.1 mi.

To Escalante 27 mi.

Well-formed crystals of selenite, a variety of gypsum, can be obtained in the region illustrated on the accompanying map. To get to this fairly accessible site, go east on Highway 12 about four and one-half miles from Escalante and then turn south onto Hole-In-The-Rock Road. This road is well graded, and should present no problems, but there are a few sandy spots where care should be taken. Four-wheel drive isn't necessary, but a good rugged vehicle would certainly be a good choice.

Go south about five miles to where the road crosses Harris Wash. Shortly thereafter you will be rising onto Tenmile Flat, and it is within the associated roadcuts, primarily to the east, where the selenite seams will be spotted. The gypsum is fairly easy to see, since it appears almost white, vividly contrasting with the surrounding host rock. Simply park off the road and use a chisel and a rock pick to expose portions large enough to be carefully broken off. Remember that gypsum is very fragile and soft, so be as cautious and delicate as you can, trying not to scratch or otherwise damage what you remove.

Once you have inspected a number of the road cuts and gathered some good specimens, be certain to pack them very securely. Otherwise, you will very likely return home and find selenite dust, rather than the beautiful crystallized material that you remembered gathering.

HARRIS WASH

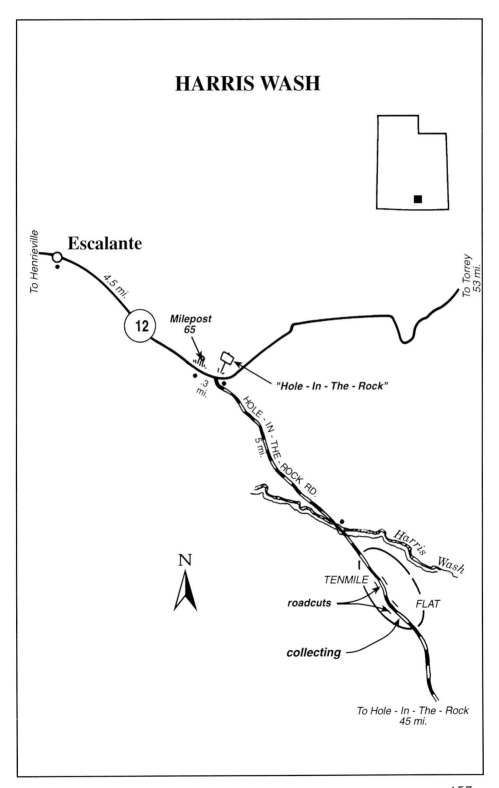

To Henrieville

Escalante

4.5 mi.

12

Milepost 65

.3 mi.

"Hole - In - The - Rock"

HOLE - IN - THE - ROCK RD.

5 mi.

To Torrey 53 mi.

N

Harris Wash

TENMILE

roadcuts

FLAT

collecting

To Hole - In - The - Rock 45 mi.

Numerous spectacular panoramas are provided along the route to this fossil collecting site, as the road winds its way alongside the mighty Colorado River for quite a distance. To get there from Moab, go west on Kane Creek Road, which intersects Highway 191 just south of town. The pavement ends after having gone about five miles but the road is well graded all the way to the collecting site.

At the ten mile mark, there is a major intersection and you should bear right toward Hurrah Pass, on Kane Springs Road. Beyond Hurrah Pass, the road becomes Lockhart Basin Road, and drops down toward the Colorado before swinging southward toward Highway 211. Approximately twenty-four miles from Highway 191, thin layers of gray limestone can be spotted within the orange cliffs and hills on either side of the road, but primarily to the east. The limestone is easy to spot, since the color strongly contrasts with the surrounding orange and red native rock.

Pull off the road and carefully scramble to the limestone regions. If you don't feel like climbing around in the hills, inspect limestone that has been weathered away and deposited on the lowlands, since that material is just as likely to provide great specimens as something taken directly from the primary deposit. The surface might be slightly more weathered, however, but careful splitting and trimming with hammer and chisel can usually remedy that situation. This site is quite remote, so be sure somebody knows where you are going and when you are expected back, especially if you are traveling alone.

LOCKHART BASIN

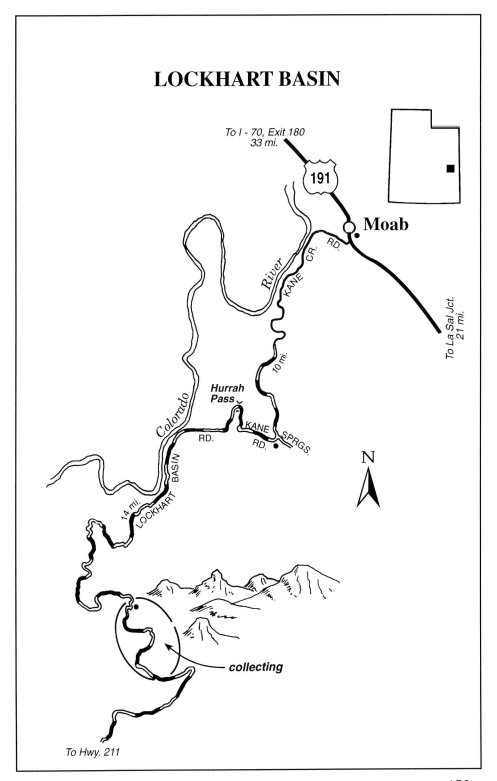

To I - 70, Exit 180
33 mi.

191

Moab

River

KANE CR. RD.

To La Sal Jct.
21 mi.

10 mi.

Colorado

Hurrah
Pass

KANE
RD.

SPRGS.

RD.

14 mi. LOCKHART BASIN

N

collecting

To Hwy. 211

Fossils abound throughout the southeast quarter of Utah, but most deposits are difficult to get to. The two sites described here are exceptions, however, and provide collectors with an opportunity to gather a good variety with very little effort. Of primary interest at these locations are well preserved crinoid stems, crinoid cups, horn corals, ammonites, trilobites, and brachiopods.

To get to Site A, go north from Moab, on Highway 191, about two miles to the Colorado River bridge and then continue north another two and four-tenths miles. There, almost directly across from the Arches National Park Visitors' Center is the collecting spot. Just park in a safe place, well off the road, and hike toward the hills on the west side of the pavement. It is easy to see the gray, fossil-bearing limestone from down below, which marks your final destination. If you don't feel like scrambling around on the hillsides, plenty of fossils can be found down below, already completely or partially weathered out of the host rock.

The best way to gather the flatland specimens is to get down on your hands and knees and crawl around looking for shells, corals, and crinoid stems. You can gather quite a good quantity in a relatively short amount of time. If you want your fossils still embedded in the host limestone, break up chunks that have weathered loose or attack the primary deposits directly, with hard rock tools, including sledge hammers, gads, pry bars and chisels.

To get to Site B, double back on Highway 191 seven-tenths of a mile and go west on Highway 279 about sixteen and one-half miles. This is a very scenic drive, as the road parallels the Colorado River most of the way. About one and one-half miles past the massive potash mine there are some little hills on the right, and it is within those hills that more crinoids and corals can be gathered, either still encased within the limestone or loose in the sand. There is a jeep trail heading through the site, and if your vehicle is capable, it might be fruitful to follow it a few tenths of a mile, stopping from time to time to see what can be found. Site B tends to offer a better variety than Site A, but both locations are very productive.

POTASH ROAD

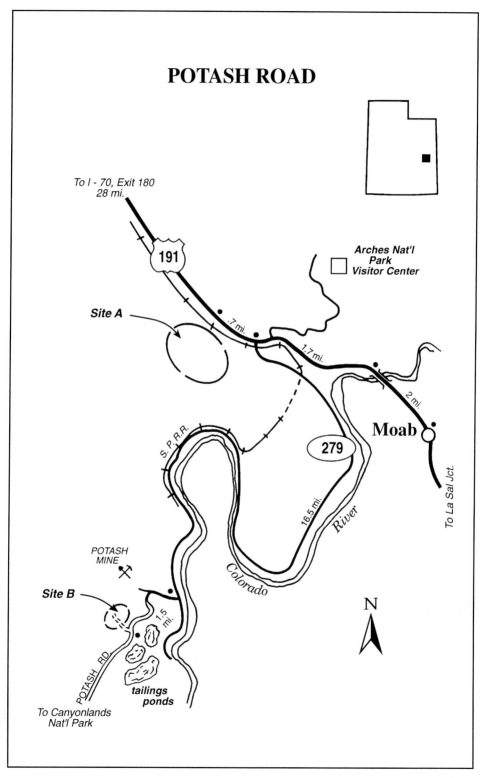

To I - 70, Exit 180
28 mi.

191

Site A

.7 mi.

1.7 mi.

Arches Nat'l Park
Visitor Center

2 mi.

Moab

279

To La Sal Jct.

S. P. R. R.

16.5 mi.

River

Colorado

POTASH MINE

Site B

1.5 mi.

N

tailings ponds

POTASH RD.

To Canyonlands Nat'l Park

The location illustrated on the accompanying map provides collectors with good quantities of often colorful agate. To get there, however, a rugged four-wheel drive vehicle is probably essential, due to the frequently encountered loose sand and rough roads.

With that in mind, go north from Moab, on Highway 191, about fifteen miles. Just before crossing Courthouse Wash, there is a dirt road leading off to the west. That road is somewhat difficult to see, especially when driving north, so it might be necessary to continue over Courthouse Wash and double back, which will also provide a safer exit from the highway.

After leaving the pavement, you will cross the railroad tracks and, at the one-half mile mark, there will be a fork. Bear left at that and the next fork, which is an additional one-half mile along the way. Continuing another one and one-half miles, turn right off the main road, and proceed about three more miles. At that point, you should be northeast of prominent Merrimac Butte, in the middle of Courthouse Pasture. Be advised that there are many intersecting roads and ruts all along the final three mile stretch, and it is often most difficult to determine which is the main road. The key is to simply head toward Merrimac Butte, rather than worry about remaining on the primary set of tracks.

When in Courthouse Pasture, park just about anywhere and explore the surrounding terrain. If you have little or no luck at the first stop, drive a little farther and try again. The agate is fairly easy to spot, due to its whitish appearance, which contrasts vividly with the reddish-orange soil. Some of the agate is colorful and filled with intricate little inclusions. Other pieces, however, aren't very interesting at all.

COURTHOUSE PASTURE

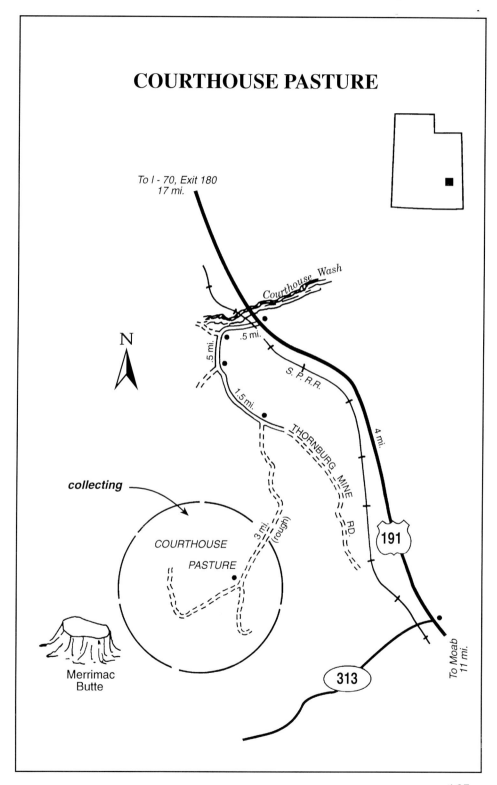

To I - 70, Exit 180
17 mi.

Courthouse Wash

N

.5 mi.

.5 mi.

S. P. R. R.

1.5 mi.

THORNBURG MINE RD.

4 mi.

collecting

3 mi.
(rough)

COURTHOUSE
PASTURE

191

313

Merrimac
Butte

To Moab
11 mi.

Both of the sites illustrated on the accompanying map provide the gem hunter with lots of top quality agate. To get to Site A, take Exit 89 from Interstate 70, which is about thirty-seven miles east of Salina, and head south. Less than one-tenth of mile from the interstate, a dirt road heads off to the east and there is a sign designating it to be the route to Last Chance Ranch. Follow that road about two miles and then bear right another five miles to Willow Springs Wash.

Getting in and out of this sandy gully is often steep and precarious, especially if there have been recent heavy rains. In fact, if the banks are severely eroded, you may find yourself having to either abort the trip or partake in some road repair work, even if you have a rugged four-wheel drive unit.

Just past the wash is a fork with a sign providing mileage to Mussentuchit Dunes. At the sign bear left about two and three-tenths more miles to where, on the right, there is a small pond. Be advised that this "pond" is often dry and is nothing more than an alkali-stained depression in the soil. It marks the center of Site A. Park off the road and hike around. Agate chips and small specimens are scattered throughout the terrain, but the best and largest material is usually found a few hundred yards south, in the little gully.

To get to Site B, return to the fork near Willow Springs Wash. This time take what would have originally been the right branch. Go about four and one-half miles and just before crossing Last Chance Wash rough ruts will be seen leading off to the right. Follow them a few tenths of a mile to the hills and park. This is the center of Site B.

Site B boasts slightly more colorful material than Site A, including a spectacular red variety. Search among the native basalt and look for outcrops on some of the surrounding hillsides. Don't hesitate to do a little walking. Be advised that much of the material is severely fractured. Lots of good clean material can still be found, however, by those willing to put forth the time and effort to find it.

WILLOW SPRINGS WASH

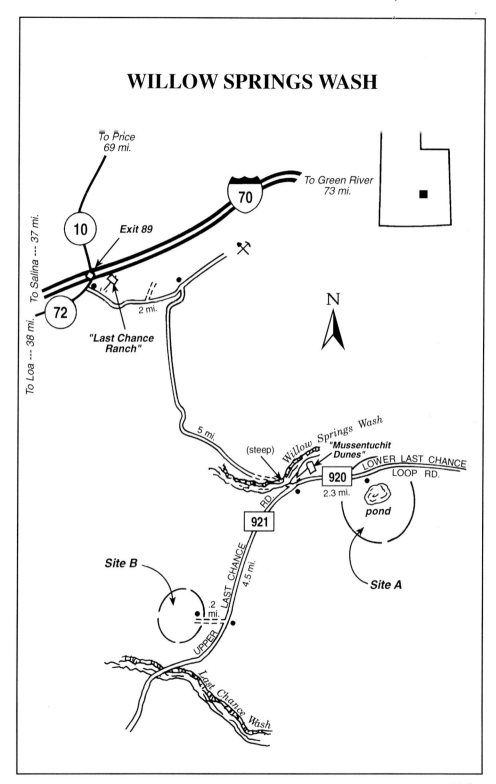

MINERAL LOCATOR INDEX

MINERAL LOCATOR INDEX